The Essential CALVIN AND HOBBES

A Calvin and Hobbes Treasury

Bill Watterson

SCHOLASTIC INC.

New York Toronto London Auckland Sydney

Calvin and Hobbes is distributed internationally by Universal Press Syndicate.

ISBN 0-590-81924-0

12 11   9/0

Printed in the U.S.A.   08
First Scholastic printing, September 1998

Foreword

Bill Watterson draws wonderful bedside tables. I admire that. He also draws great water splashes and living room couches and chairs and lamps and yawns and screams, and all the things that make a comic strip fun to look at. I like the thin little arms on Calvin and his shoes that look like dinner rolls.

Drawing in a comic strip is infinitely more important than we may think, for our medium must compete with other entertainments, and if a cartoonist does nothing more than illustrate a joke, he or she is going to lose.

Calvin and Hobbes, however, contains hilarious pictures that cannot be duplicated in other mediums. In short, it is fun to look at, and that is what has made Bill's work such an admirable success.

— CHARLES M. SCHULZ

To Tom

Suddenly a floorboard creak
Announces the bloodsucking freak
Is here to steal my future years away!
A sulf'rous smell now fills the room
Heralding my imm'nent doom!
A fang gleams in the dark and murky gray!

Oh, blood-red eyes and tentacles!
Throbbing, pulsing ventricles!
Mucus-oozing pores and frightful claws!

Worse, in terms of outright scariness,
Are the suckers multifarious
That grab and force you in its mighty jaws!

This disgusting aberration
Of nature needs no motivation
To devour helpless children in their beds.
Relishing despairing moans,
It chews kids up and sucks their bones,
And dissolves inside its mouth their li'l heads!

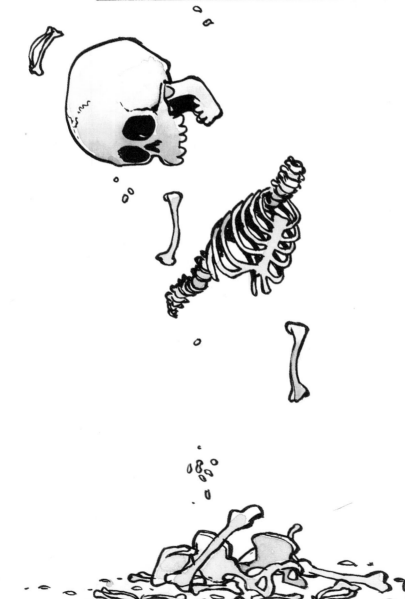

I know this 'cause I read it not
Two hours ago, and then I got
The heebie-jeebies and these awful shakes.

My parents swore upon their honor
That I was safe, and not a goner.
I guess tomorrow they'll see their sad mistakes.

Dad will look at Mom and say,
"Too bad he had to go that way."
And Mom will look at Dad, and nod assent.

Mom will add, "Still, it's fitting,
That as he was this world quitting,
He should leave another mess before he went."

They may not mind at first, I know.
They will miss me later, though,
And perhaps admit that they were wrong.
As memories of me grow dim,
They'll say, "We were too strict with him.
We should have listened to him all along."

Here Lies
CALVIN
DEVOURED IN HIS
BED BY A MONSTER

If Only We Had
Treated Him Better

As speedily my end approaches,
I bid a final "buenas noches"
To my best friend here in all the world.
Gently snoring, whiskers seeming
To sniff at smells (he must be dreaming),
He lies snuggled in the blankets, curled.

SO LONG, POP! I'M OFF TO CHECK MY TIGER TRAP!

I RIGGED A TUNA FISH SANDWICH YESTERDAY, SO I'M **SURE** TO HAVE A TIGER BY NOW!

THEY LIKE TUNA FISH, HUH?

TIGERS WILL DO **ANYTHING** FOR A TUNA FISH SANDWICH!

WE'RE KIND OF STUPID THAT WAY.

MUNCH MUNCH

SO DAD, WHAT DO I DO WHEN I CATCH A TIGER?

BRING IT HOME AND STUFF IT, CALVIN! CAN'T YOU SEE I'M BUSY?

SHEESH.

NO, REALLY, I COULDN'T EAT ANOTHER BITE!

WHAT'S ALL THIS NOISE? YOU'RE SUPPOSED TO BE ASLEEP!

IT WAS HOBBES, DAD! HE WAS JUMPING ON THE BED! HONEST!

"HOBBES" WAS **NOT** JUMPING ON THE BED! NOW GO TO SLEEP!

YOU WERE **TOO** JUMPING ON THE BED!

WELL, **YOU** WERE THE ONE PLAYING THE CYMBALS!!

Calvin and Hobbes by WATTERSON

OUTRAGE! WHY SHOULD I GO TO BED? I'M NOT TIRED! IT'S ONLY 7:30! THIS IS TYRANNY! I'M!

ZZZZ

GOOD NIGHT, CALVIN.

WILL YOU CHECK FOR MONSTERS UNDER THE BED?

NO MONSTERS. YOU'RE SAFE.

WHAT ABOUT IN THE DRESSER?

CALVIN, I'M SURE THERE ARE NO MONSTERS IN YOUR DRESSER. GO TO SLEEP.

GREAT. I'LL BET THAT'S WHERE THEY ALL ARE. THEY'LL COME OUT AND KILL US AS SOON AS WE FALL ASLEEP.

SO WHO'S GOING TO FALL ASLEEP?

WELL, WE'LL JUST HAVE TO GET THE MONSTERS FIRST. YOU IRRITATE THEM WITH THIS HORN, AND I'LL NAIL 'EM WITH MY DART GUN WHEN THEY COME OUT!

GET READY! I HEAR ONE COMING!

HONK HONK HONK HONK HON HOA HONK

WHAT'S ALL THE NOISE?!

AAIEEE!! A MONSTER IN THE HALLWAY!!

DEAR, WILL YOU COME UP HERE A MINUTE?

I THINK I WOUNDED HIM. GIVE ME THE BAT AND I'LL FINISH HIM OFF!

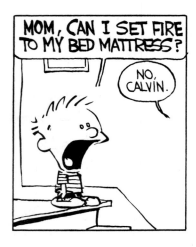

Calvin and Hobbes
by WATTERSON

WE JOIN OUR HERO MEGAZORKS ABOVE PLANET GLOOB...

SPACEMAN SPIFF, CONQUEROR OF THE COSMOS, IS PURSUED BY THE HIDEOUS SCUM BEINGS OF PLANET Q-13!

SPIFF'S HYPER-FREEM DRIVE MALFUNCTIONS! THE ALIENS CLOSE IN!

SUDDENLY, A SEARING BOLT OF DEADLY FRAP RAY SLICES ACROSS THE BLACKNESS! OUR HERO IS UNFAZED.

ANOTHER BOLT! SPIFF IS HIT!!

PLOOIE!

SPIFF IS GOING DOWN! CAN HE MAKE IT?? IS THIS THE END?!?

AAAAAA

SPIFF'S ALIVE! HE MADE IT!!

WATTERSON

I'M ALIVE! HA HA HA! I KISS THE SWEET GROUND!

MAYBE YOU SHOULD PLAY ON THE SWINGS, CALVIN.

IT SAYS HERE THAT BY THE AGE OF SIX ...

.. MOST CHILDREN HAVE SEEN A MILLION MURDERS ON TELEVISION.

I FIND THAT VERY DISTURBING!

IT MEANS I'VE BEEN WATCHING ALL THE WRONG CHANNELS.

I'M NOT EATING THIS GREEN STUFF. YECCHH!

GOOD IDEA, CALVIN. IT'S A PLATE OF TOXIC WASTE THAT WILL TURN YOU INTO A MUTANT IF YOU EAT IT.

RRGHHMPHFFG

MMMM SCRAPE URF GLUNK SMACK URF YUM

THERE HAS **GOT** TO BE A BETTER WAY TO MAKE HIM EAT!

AHHHH.. I CAN FEEL IT WORKING..

DAD, HOW COME YOU LIVE IN THIS HOUSE WITH MOM...

.. INSTEAD OF IN AN APARTMENT WITH SEVERAL SCANTILY CLAD FEMALE ROOMMATES?

BOY! ASK A SIMPLE QUESTION, AND GET ALL YOUR TELEVISION PRIVILEGES REVOKED.

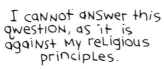

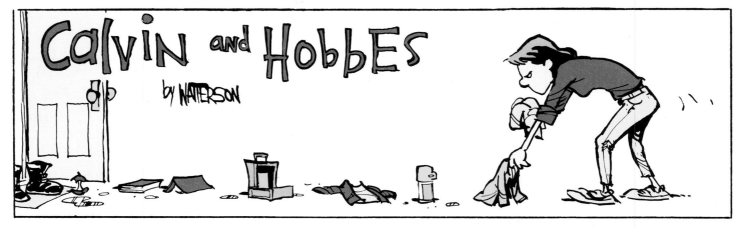

HI, DAD. IT'S ME, CALVIN!

HOW'S WORK GOING? ...UH HUH... PRETTY DAY OUT, ISN'T IT? ... YEP.....

ARE YOU BRINGING ME HOME ANY PRESENTS TONIGHT? ... NO? WELL, JUST THOUGHT I'D ASK...

LISTEN, I SUPPOSE YOU'RE WONDERING WHY I CALLED...

DAD, YOUR POLLS TOOK A BIG DIVE THIS WEEK.

YOUR "OVERALL DAD PERFORMANCE" RATING WAS ESPECIALLY LOW.

SEE? RIGHT ABOUT YESTERDAY YOUR POPULARITY WENT DOWN THE TUBES.

CALVIN, YOU DIDN'T GET DESSERT YESTERDAY BECAUSE YOU FLOODED THE HOUSE!!

I'D SUGGEST A NEW LINE OF WORK, "DAD"!..

THE GIANT SLIMY OCTOPUS OOZES ACROSS THE BEACH.

HIS HIDEOUS PRESENCE TERRORIZES THE SLEEPY WATERFRONT COMMUNITY.

WITH A SUCKER-COVERED TENTACLE, HE GRABS AN UNSUSPECTING TOURIST.

A MUFFLED SCREAM LINGERS IN THE SALTY AIR!

DID YOU WANT SOMETHING, CALVIN?

ACK ICK IG

Calvin and Hobbes
by Watterson

WHAT SHOULD WE HAVE DAD READ US TONIGHT?

..SO IN THE NEXT PANEL, SUPERTOAD GOES "PLOOIE", AND...

" 'MY, WHAT BIG TEETH YOU HAVE!' SAID LITTLE RED RIDING HOOD. 'THE BETTER TO EAT YOU WITH!' SAID THE WOLF..."

TIGER.

"...SAID THE TIGER, AND HE POUNCED ON LITTLE RED RIDING HOOD."

" JUST THEN A HUNTER CAME BY, AND WHEN HE SAW THE WOLF..."

TIGER.

"..WHEN HE SAW THE TIGER, HE PICKED UP HIS GUN AND..."

..AND?

"...AND IT WAS TOO LATE. THE TIGER ATE THEM BOTH AND HE LIVED HAPPILY EVER AFTER. THE END."

GOOD STORY, DAD! THANKS!

SNIFF I ALWAYS CRY AT HAPPY ENDINGS.

"A BUSHEL IS A UNIT OF WEIGHT EQUAL TO FOUR PECKS."

WHAT'S A PECK?

A QUICK SMOOCH.

YOU KNOW, I DON'T UNDERSTAND MATH AT ALL.

MOM, CAN I HAVE SOME MONEY SO HOBBES AND I CAN GO TO A MOVIE?

WHAT MOVIE?

"THE CUISINART MURDERER OF CENTRAL HIGH."

I REALLY THINK THERE ARE MORE CONSTRUCTIVE WAYS YOU COULD SPEND YOUR AFTERNOON, CALVIN.

WHAT DID SHE SAY?

OH, SHE WENT OFF ON ONE OF HER IRRELEVANT TANGENTS AGAIN.

DO YOU BELIEVE OUR DESTINIES ARE CONTROLLED BY THE STARS?

NO, I THINK WE CAN DO WHATEVER WE WANT WITH OUR LIVES.

NOT TO HEAR MOM AND DAD TELL IT.

I'D LIKE TO GET A VALENTINE BOUQUET FOR A GIRL I KNOW.

WHAT A SWEET LITTLE BOY YOU ARE! COME SEE WHAT WE HAVE.

IS THIS ALL?

DID YOU HAVE SOMETHING SPECIAL IN MIND?

SORT OF. DO YOU HAVE A DUMPSTER OUT BACK I COULD ROOT THROUGH?

CALVIN, YOU BALONEY BRAIN!

YOU SENT ME A HATE-MAIL VALENTINE AND A CRUMMY BUNCH OF DEAD FLOWERS!

SO HERE'S A VALENTINE FOR *YOU*, YOU INSENSITIVE CLOD!!

POW

A VALENTINE AND FLOWERS! HE *LIKES* ME!

SHE NOTICED! SHE *LIKES* ME!

Hey, Calvin, it's gonna cost you 50 cents to be my friend today.

AND WHAT IF I DON'T *WANT* TO BE YOUR FRIEND TODAY?

Then the janitor scrapes you off the wall with a spatula.

HECK, WHAT'S A LITTLE EXTORTION AMONG FRIENDS?

I GOT THE NEW ALBUM BY SCRAMBLED DEBUTANTE.

ALL THEIR SONGS GLORIFY DEPRAVED VIOLENCE, MINDLESS SEX, AND THE DELIBERATE ABUSE OF DANGEROUS DRUGS.

YOUR MOM'S GOING TO GO INTO CONNIPTIONS WHEN SHE SEES *THIS* LYING AROUND.

WELL I SURE DIDN'T BUY IT FOR THE MUSIC..

MOM, WILL YOU DRIVE ME INTO TOWN?

WHY SHOULD I *DRIVE* YOU, CALVIN? IT'S A PERFECT DAY OUTSIDE!

WHAT DO YOU THINK PEOPLE HAVE *FEET* FOR?

TO WORK THE GAS PEDAL.

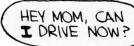

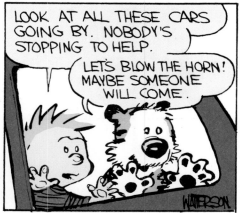

You're gonna taste asphalt fifth period, Twinky. Just so you know.

GREAT. I'M DEAD.

FIFTH PERIOD—"STUDIES IN CONTEMPORARY STATE-SPONSORED TERRORISM."

...ALSO KNOWN AS GYM CLASS.

I CAN'T GET A BABY SITTER ANYWHERE! WHAT SHOULD WE DO?

WE WON'T BE GONE LONG. COULDN'T CALVIN BE LEFT FOR A COUPLE HOURS UNSUPERVISED?

HA HA HA HA HA! HO HO HO HO HO HEE HE HA HOO HO HO HA HA

...SERIOUSLY... WHAT SHOULD WE DO?

HEE HEE

OKAY, CALVIN, WE'LL BE BACK IN A COUPLE OF HOURS.

YOU AND HOBBES JUST WATCH TV AND BE GOOD, OKAY?

DID YOU HEAR THAT? WE GET TO WATCH TV!!

HOORAY!

VIDEORAMA? I'D LIKE TO RENT A VCR AND SOME MOVIES!

ASK IF THEY HAVE "ATTACK OF THE COED CANNIBALS."

Calvin and Hobbes
by WATTERSON

TOLL BOOTH, DAD! YOU CAN'T PUT THE CAR IN UNTIL YOU PAY ME A QUARTER!

WHY SHOULD I PAY YOU TO PUT *MY* CAR IN *MY* GARAGE?

BECAUSE IF YOU DON'T, I'LL PULL THE DOOR DOWN ON THE HOOD AS YOU DRIVE IN!

WHAT A CHEAPSKATE.

A LITTLE LOWER...OK, FINE!

THANKS FOR HELPING ME PUT UP THIS SWING.

WHERE DID YOU EVER FIND THIS GREAT TIRE?

CALVIN! I'VE GOT TO GO TO WORK!!

WHAT'S THAT CEREAL YOU'RE EATING?

IT'S MY NEW FAVORITE, "CHOCOLATE FROSTED SUGAR BOMBS."

HAVE A TASTE.

THANK YOU.

MFFPBTH!! S-SW-SW SWEET!!

ACTUALLY, THEY'RE KINDA BLAND TILL YOU SCOOP SUGAR ON 'EM.

SOMEWHERE IN COMMUNIST RUSSIA I'LL BET THERE'S A LITTLE BOY WHO HAS NEVER KNOWN ANYTHING BUT **CENSORSHIP** AND **OPPRESSION**.

BUT MAYBE HE'S HEARD ABOUT **AMERICA**, AND HE DREAMS OF LIVING IN THIS LAND OF **FREEDOM** AND OPPORTUNITY!

SOMEDAY, I'D LIKE TO MEET THAT LITTLE BOY...

...AND TELL HIM THE AWFUL **TRUTH** ABOUT THIS PLACE!!

CALVIN, BE QUIET AND EAT THE STUPID LIMA BEANS.

WHENEVER I TAKE MY BATH...

...I ALWAYS PUT MY DUCKY IN FIRST.

FOR COMPANIONSHIP?

TO TEST FOR SHARKS.

MY SECRET ANCIENT TREASURE MAP SAYS TO DIG HERE!

LOOK! A WALLET FULL OF MONEY! RIGHT WHERE YOU SAID!

IT'S DAD'S. I BURIED IT HERE LAST WEEK.

SPACEMAN SPIFF, BOLD INTERPLANETARY EXPLORER, SPIES A ZARG!

SPIFF CALIBRATES HIS BLASTER. READY...AIM...

CALVIN, IF YOU SHOOT THAT PAPER CLIP AT ME, I'LL GET YOUR BOTTOM HAULED TO THE PRINCIPAL'S OFFICE SO FAST YOU'LL THINK YOU WERE IN A **TIME WARP**!!

CONFOUND IT. THE BLASTER JAMMED.

IT LOOKS LIKE HOBBES BURST A SEAM HERE. I'LL GET MY SEWING KIT.

IT'S JUST A LITTLE CUT. I DON'T NEED AN OPERATION. THIS IS UNNECESSARY SURGERY!

IT'S NOT SURGERY. YOU'RE JUST GETTING A COUPLE STITCHES! WHAT'S THE BIG DEAL?

YOUR MOM NEVER USES ANY ANESTHETIC.

WHAT A PECULIAR DREAM I HAD LAST NIGHT!

I DREAMED I WAS IN A BIG FIGHT WITH A FEROCIOUS WEASEL!

WHAT DO YOU SUPPOSE IT MEANS?

IT MEANS YOU'RE SLEEPING ON THE FLOOR TONIGHT, YOU NINCOMPOOP!

WHY CAN'T I STAY UP LATE? YOU GUYS CAN!

IT'S NOT FAIR!

THE *WORLD* ISN'T FAIR, CALVIN.

I KNOW, BUT WHY ISN'T IT EVER UNFAIR IN MY FAVOR?

THE VALIANT SPACEMAN SPIFF IS BEING PURSUED BY A DISGUSTING SCUM BEING!

SPIFF SPOTS HIS HOVERING SPACESHIP AND BOLTS FOR THE LADDER!

BUT HE'S TOO LATE! THE AWFUL SCUM BEING IS UPON HIM! IT'S ALL OVER!

IT'S ALL OVER!!

I TOLD YOU **THREE TIMES** RECESS WAS OVER! NOW GET INSIDE!

AS DICTATOR, I HAVE THE SOLE VOICE IN GOVERNMENT!

I WILL NOT TOLERATE DISSENT!

I ALONE SHALL DECIDE THE GOOD! I ALONE SHALL...

TIME FOR BED, CALVIN.

COULDN'T WE VOTE ON THIS?

IF YOU COULD WISH FOR ANYTHING, WHAT WOULD IT BE?

A BIG SUNNY FIELD TO BE IN.

A **STUPID FIELD?!** YOU'VE GOT THAT NOW! THINK **BIG**! RICHES! POWER! PRETEND YOU COULD HAVE **ANYTHING**!

ACTUALLY, IT'S HARD TO ARGUE WITH SOMEONE WHO LOOKS SO HAPPY.

Z

HERE FISH!

THEY MUST KNOW THAT ONE.

AAGHH!

CHOMP!

ARE THE FISH BITING?

DROP DEAD, HOBBES.

I CAN'T GET THIS MODEL AIRPLANE TO LOOK RIGHT.

THESE DIRECTIONS ARE IMPOSSIBLE!

RRRRRGGGHHHHH WHAM WHAM WHAM

HIT BY ANTI-AIRCRAFT GUNS.

YOUR PLANES DO SEEM TO RUN INTO THOSE, DON'T THEY?

TOMMY TOLD A FUNNY STORY AT SCHOOL TODAY. I ALMOST DIED!

TELL IT TO ME.

WELL, ACTUALLY THE STORY ITSELF WASN'T SO FUNNY...

...IT WAS THE *WAY* HE TOLD IT.

HOW DID HE TELL IT?

HE WAS DRINKING MILK AND WHEN HE LAUGHED, IT CAME UP HIS NOSE!

You've got two periods to live, Twinky.

Then it's gym class, and I turn you into hamburger casserole!

I HATE GYM CLASS.

COACH THINKS VIOLENCE IS AEROBIC.

WOW! ANOTHER HOLE IN ONE!

WOW! THREE NEW MAGAZINES FOR ME TODAY.

YESTERDAY I GOT FIVE. I LOVE GETTING ALL THIS MAIL.

HOW COME YOU RECEIVE ALL THESE MAGAZINES?

I WENT TO THE LIBRARY AND FILLED OUT ALL THE SUBSCRIPTION CARDS THAT SAID "BILL ME LATER."

I LOVE SATURDAY MORNING CARTOONS.

WHAT CLASSIC HUMOR!

THIS IS WHAT ENTERTAINMENT IS ALL ABOUT.

... IDIOTS, EXPLOSIVES, AND FALLING ANVILS.

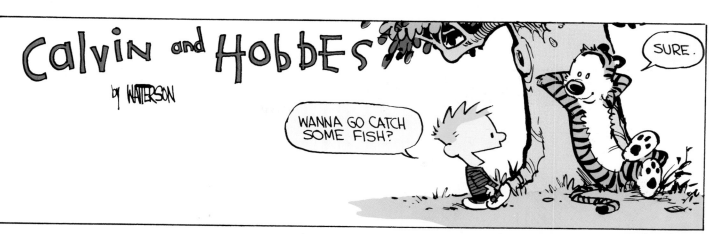

CALVIN, THE HUMAN INSECT, WALKS ACROSS THE DINNER TABLE.

WITH PROPORTIONAL INSECT STRENGTH, HE PLACES A GIANT PEA ON THE EDGE OF A SPOON.

HE THEN CLIMBS TO THE TOP OF THE OTHER END...

...AND WITH A TINY JUMP...

CALVIN, STOP THAT!

IN HIS MINUSCULE SIZE, IT TAKES CALVIN, THE HUMAN INSECT, TEN MINUTES TO WALK ACROSS A BOOK'S PAGE!

AT THE OTHER END, HE SLOWLY LIFTS THE GIGANTIC SHEET!

THEN IT'S ANOTHER TEN-MINUTE JOURNEY BACK, AS HE TURNS IT OVER!

GEE, THE KID'S BEEN QUIET FOR ALMOST TWENTY MINUTES.

HE'S DOING HIS HOMEWORK.

HERE'S A MOVIE WE SHOULD WATCH.

WHO'S IN IT?

IT SAYS, "JAPANESE CAST."

"TWO BIG RUBBERY MONSTERS SLUG IT OUT OVER MAJOR METROPOLITAN CENTERS IN A BATTLE FOR WORLD SUPREMACY."

DOESN'T THAT SOUND GREAT?

AND PEOPLE SAY THAT FOREIGN FILM IS INACCESSIBLE.

GRAB THE HOTDOGS AND COME ON!

THE TROOP'S COOKING DINNER OVER THE FIRE.

OH THAT'S JUST GREAT.

HERE WE'VE BEEN LUGGING THIS DUMB MICROWAVE AROUND FOR NOTHING.

BOP

SPIKE!

OH OH, WE'D BETTER LEAVE!

IT LOOKS LIKE SOME BIG PEOPLE WANT TO PLAY TENNIS.

THE CROCODILE FLOATS TO THE TOP OF THE MURKY AMAZON...

COMPLETELY MOTIONLESS, HE APPEARS TO BE ONLY A HARMLESS LOG.

A HIPPOPOTAMUS APPROACHES AND ENSURES ITS INSTANT DEATH!

CALVIN, WHAT ARE YOU DOING? ARE YOU ALL RIGHT?

CLOSER... CLOSER...

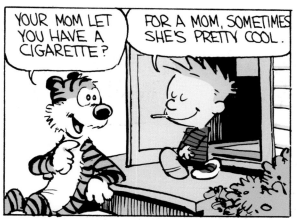

MOM! MOM! A BIG DOG KNOCKED ME DOWN AND HE STOLE HOBBES!

I TRIED TO CATCH HIM, BUT I COULDN'T, AND NOW I'VE LOST MY BEST FRIEND!

WELL CALVIN, IF YOU WOULDN'T DRAG THAT TIGER EVERYWHERE, THINGS LIKE THIS WOULDN'T HAPPEN.

THERE'S NO PROBLEM SO AWFUL THAT YOU CAN'T ADD SOME GUILT TO IT AND MAKE IT EVEN WORSE!

I CAN'T SLEEP AT ALL. POOR HOBBES! I WONDER WHERE HE IS. I HOPE HE'S OK.

SNIFF.. WHAT DID I EVER DO TO DESERVE THIS?

WHATEVER IT WAS, I'M SORRY ALREADY!

LOST: MY TIGER, "HOBBES"

MAYBE YOU SHOULD DESCRIBE HIM.

ON THE QUIET SIDE. SOMEWHAT PECULIAR. A GOOD COMPANION, IN A WEIRD SORT OF WAY.

I MEAN, WHAT DOES HE LOOK LIKE?

OH.

SUSIE, WANNA HEAR A SECRET?

SURE.

I THINK THE PRINCIPAL IS A SPACE ALIEN SPY.

HE'S TRYING TO CORRUPT OUR YOUNG INNOCENT MINDS SO WE'LL BE UNABLE TO RESIST WHEN HIS PEOPLE INVADE EARTH!

PROMISE NOT TO TELL ANYONE?

DON'T WORRY.

HOBBES, WHAT SHOULD I DO WHEN MOE COMES TO BEAT ME UP IN GYM CLASS?

WELL, YOU CAN ALWAYS DO WHAT WE TIGERS DO WHEN A RHINO CHARGES.

WHAT'S THAT?

WE SCRAMBLE LIKE MANIACS FOR THE NEAREST TREE.

THAT'S YOUR ADVICE?? TO SIT IN A TREE ALL DAY?!?

IT DOESN'T IMPRESS THE GIRLS, OF COURSE, BUT THERE'S NO SENSE IMPRESSING THEM AND THEN GETTING KILLED, MY DAD USED TO SAY...

HOBBES, I NEED YOUR HELP. THAT BULLY MOE KEEPS PUSHING ME AROUND.

...SO I WANT YOU TO COME TO SCHOOL AND EAT HIM, OK?

EAT HIM?

SURE! TIGERS EAT PEOPLE ALL THE TIME!

WHAT IF THE CAFETERIA LADIES WON'T LET ME USE THE OVEN?

IT'S TOO EARLY TO BE IN BED. IT'S HARDLY EVEN DARK OUT. WHY DO I HAVE TO BE IN BED? IT'S RIDICULOUS.

I'M NOT EVEN TIRED! I DON'T NEED TO BE IN BED! THIS IS AN OUTRAGE!

IT'S THE STUPIDEST THING I CAN IMAGINE! I THINK MOM AND DAD ARE JUST TRYING TO GET RID OF ME. I CAN'T SLEEP AT ALL. CAN YOU SLEEP, HOBBES?

NO!

WATTERSON

OK, MOM, HOBBES AND I HAVE FORMED A LOBBY. WE WANT MORE PRIVILEGES!

MORE PRIVILEGES? LIKE WHAT? YOU'VE GOT IT MADE!

NO RESPONSIBILITIES, NO CARES, NO WORRIES! WHAT MORE COULD YOU POSSIBLY WANT?

WHY DIDN'T YOU TELL HER ABOUT THE CREDIT CARDS IN OUR NAMES?

YOU HEARD HER. SHE'S IN ONE OF HER MOODS.

I LOVE SATURDAYS!

EVERY SATURDAY I GET UP AT SIX AND EAT THREE BOWLS OF CRUNCHY SUGAR BOMBS.

THEN I WATCH CARTOONS TILL NOON, AND I'M INCOHERENT AND HYPERACTIVE THE REST OF THE DAY.

DOES IT WORK?

NO BROTHERS OR SISTERS SO FAR!

IN THE COMMERCIALS, THIS COLA GREATLY INCREASES ONE'S SEX APPEAL.

GLIK GLIK GLICK GLICK

WATTERSON

BUR-UR-URPP!!

EVIDENTLY A LITTLE LICENSE ON MADISON AVENUE'S PART.

PHOO! RIGHT UP MY NOSE.

IT'S AN OUTRAGE THAT SIX-YEAR-OLDS CAN'T VOTE!

HERE I AM, A U.S. CITIZEN, WITH NO VOICE IN OUR REPRESENTATIVE GOVERNMENT!

YOU'RE CONCERNED ABOUT THE DIRECTION THE COUNTRY IS HEADED?

NO, I JUST WANT A BIGGER PIECE OF THE PIE.

WATTERSON

POOF POOF POOF

POW!

GOOD HEAVENS, I THINK I BLEW MY FACE INSIDE OUT!

WATTERSON

THE WATER'S TOO COLD!

NOW IT'S TOO HOT.

NOW IT'S TOO COLD.

NOW IT'S TOO DEEP.

THE FEARSOME SHARK SENSES DISTRESS IN THE WAVES ABOVE HIM!

HE CIRCLES UP, CLOSER AND CLOSER TO THE TERRIFIED VICTIM!

HEY! YAHH! SNAP THRASH SNAP.

YOU KNOW, FOR SOMEONE WHO HATES BATHS AS MUCH AS YOU DO, YOU'RE NOT MAKING THIS GO ANY FASTER!

ANOTHER GRUESOME KILL..

HERE, CALVIN, I'LL SHOW YOU A MAGIC TRICK.

SEE? I PULLED A DIME FROM YOUR EAR! PRETTY GOOD, HUH?

ANYTHING YET?

J-JUST A B-B-BLOODY N-NOSE.

WHAT'S ALL THE RUCKUS?! YOU'RE SUPPOSED TO BE ASLEEP!

AND WHAT'S WITH ALL THESE FEATHERS?! ARE YOU TEARING UP YOUR PILLOWS?!

IT WAS INCREDIBLE, DAD! A HERD OF DUCKS FLEW IN THE WINDOW AND MOLTED! THEY LEFT WHEN THEY HEARD YOU COMING! HONEST!

NICE ALIBI, FRIZZLETOP! NO DESSERT FOR A WEEK!

YOU WANT ANOTHER PILLOW ACROSS THE KISSER? I DIDN'T HEAR *YOU* OFFER ANY BRAINSTORMS!

YOU SEE, HOBBES, *I* HAVE A WATER BALLOON, AND *YOU* DON'T.

I THEREFORE HAVE OFFENSIVE SUPERIORITY, SO YOU HAVE TO DO WHAT I SAY. WHAT DO YOU THINK OF THAT?

I THINK I'LL TAKE THIS STICK AND POKE YOUR BALLOON.

THAT'S THE TROUBLE WITH WEAPONS TECHNOLOGY. IT BECOMES OBSOLETE SO QUICKLY.

OH MY GOSH, HOBBES! **DON'T MOVE!**

WHAT? WHAT IS IT?

THE BIGGEST, UGLIEST, FUZZIEST CATERPILLAR I'VE EVER SEEN IS ABOUT TO CHOMP YOUR BOTTOM!

AAUGH! KILL IT! KILL IT!

YOW!!

WHAM!

YOU KNOW WHAT **YOUR** PROBLEM IS? YOU'VE GOT NO APPRECIATION FOR PHYSICAL HUMOR, THAT'S WHAT!

WHEN ARE WE GOING TO GET TO OUR VACATION SITE? I WANNA *BE* THERE!

CALVIN, IT'S AN EIGHT-HOUR DRIVE. WE'RE NOT EVEN OUT OF OUR STATE YET. IT'S GOING TO BE A WHILE. RELAX.

HOW MUCH LONGER *NOW*?

I TOLD YOU WE SHOULD HAVE FLOWN.

THERE'S A RESTAURANT COMING UP. WANT TO STOP?

ONLY IF THEY HAVE HAMBURGERS.

HAMBURGERS? THAT'S ALL WE'VE EATEN THIS WHOLE STUPID TRIP! HAMBURGERS, HAMBURGERS, HAMBURGERS!

I'M SICK OF HAMBURGERS! WE'RE EATING SOMETHING ELSE FOR ONCE!

TEN MILLION BOTTLES OF BEER ON THE WALL, TEN MILLION BOTTLES OF BEER...

OK! OK! HERE'S A HAMBURGER JOINT! *ARE* YOU HAPPY?!

I HAVE TO GO TO THE BATHROOM.

CALVIN, WE JUST PULLED OUT OF THE RESTAURANT. CAN'T YOU WAIT? THINK OF SOMETHING ELSE.

ALL I CAN THINK OF IS NIAGARA FALLS, AND THE HOOVER DAM, AND NOAH'S ARK, AND...

OOH BOY, NOW *I* HAVE TO GO!

NEXT YEAR I SWEAR I'LL JUST TAKE A VACATION BY MYSELF.

THAT TRIP WAS EXCRUCIATING. THANK GOODNESS WE'RE HERE.

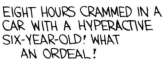

EIGHT HOURS CRAMMED IN A CAR WITH A HYPERACTIVE SIX-YEAR-OLD! WHAT AN ORDEAL!

WELL, NOW CALVIN CAN RUN AND SCREAM ALL HE LIKES. AHH, WHAT A GREAT LITTLE PLACE.

I'M BORED. WHEN ARE WE LEAVING?

YOU'RE BORED? WOULD YOU LIKE ME TO SHOW YOU HOW AN ANCHOR WORKS?

AHH! ANOTHER GLORIOUS SUNRISE, AND NOT A SOUL AROUND!

THIS IS THE LIFE! A BRISK SWIM AT DAWN, A MORNING OUT IN A BOAT...

...AND BY 9 A.M., I'M BACK WITH FRESHLY CAUGHT FISH FOR BREAKFAST! THE DAY'S HARDLY BEGUN! WHAT A VACATION!

UGH... I'VE SEEN CHEERIER FACES AT THE OFFICE!

YOU EAT YOUR DEAD ANIMALS. ALL I WANT IS SOME COFFEE.

WHY ISN'T THERE ANY TV UP HERE? I HATE THIS PLACE.

DAD, LOOK! I CAUGHT A FISH!

HEY, THAT'S A BIG ONE. I'LL SHOW YOU HOW TO CLEAN IT, AND WE'LL HAVE IT FOR DINNER.

"CLEAN IT"?

CUT OFF ITS HEAD AND GUT IT.

MMM! PASS ME ANOTHER OF THESE GREAT CHEESE SANDWICHES! HA HA, NO BONES IN THESE, RIGHT?

WOW, LOOK DOWN THERE! I THINK THAT'S THE DIM OUTLINE OF A WHALE!

I THINK THAT'S A ROCK.

AND THAT MUST BE A GIANT EEL SLITHERING UP FROM THE BOTTOM!

I THINK THAT'S A WEED.

I'LL BET THIS IS THE MAST OF AN OLD SPANISH GALLEON, SUNK HUNDREDS OF YEARS AGO.

IT'S A BRANCH.

MAN, THIS IS BORING. I WISH THERE WAS A MOVIE THEATER SOMEPLACE.

WANT TO GO FISHING?

SURE.

FISHING IS ONE SPORT I REALLY LIKE.

I CAN SEE WHY... IT'S SO CONTEMPLATIVE.

THERE'S ANOTHER ONE!!

GZZZZZZZZZZ

WAAAUUGHHH! SPLOOSH

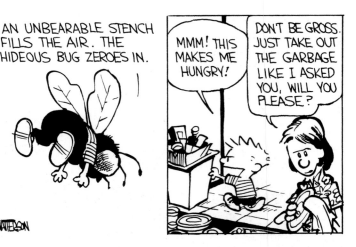

Calvin and Hobbes

by WATTERSON

IT'S ANOTHER NEW MORNING FOR MR. MONROE. HE GLANCES AT THE NEWSPAPER HEADLINES OVER A CUP OF COFFEE, AND GETS IN HIS RED SPORTS CAR TO GO TO WORK.

LITTLE DOES HE REALIZE IT'S HIS LAST DAY ON THE FACE OF THE EARTH!

CALVIN DRINKS THE MAGIC ELIXIR AND BEGINS AN INCREDIBLE TRANSFORMATION!

INSTANTLY HE GROWS! BIGGER AND BIGGER! HIGHER AND HIGHER!

HE IS NOW OVER 300 FEET TALL! THE FORMULA IS A SUCCESS!

CALVIN, THE MIGHTY GIANT, GOES ON A TERRIBLE RAMPAGE, STRIKING FEAR INTO THE HEARTS OF THE POPULACE!

NOTHING CAN STOP HIM! IT'S PANIC IN THE STREETS! A TOWN LIES IN RUINS!

NO, I WON'T BUY YOU ANY MORE TOY CARS. I SAW YOU! YOU DELIBERATELY STOMPED ON THOSE!

C'MON, CALVIN! I SIGNED YOU UP FOR SWIMMING LESSONS.

I DON'T *WANT* SWIMMING LESSONS!!

TOO LATE. LET'S GO.

WHAT ABOUT HOBBES? DID YOU SIGN HIM UP TOO?

NO, IT'S NOT GOOD TO GET TIGERS WET.

WHY IS *THAT*?

IT TAKES US ALL DAY TO DRY, AND UNTIL WE DO, WE SMELL FUNNY.

I CAN'T BELIEVE MY MOM SIGNED ME UP FOR SWIMMING LESSONS.

HERE I AM FREEZING MY BUNS OFF AT 9 IN THE MORNING, ABOUT TO JUMP INTO ICE WATER AND DROWN.

THE ONLY THING THAT COULD POSSIBLY MAKE THIS WORSE WOULD BE IF THE CLASS WAS...

...TAUGHT BY MY SADISTIC BABY SITTER!!

WELL, LOOK WHO'S HERE!

OK... EVERYONE IN THE WATER!

I REFUSE! I'M FREEZING ALREADY!

CALVIN, DO YOU KNOW WHAT A "RAT TAIL" IS?

NO.

IT'S WHEN YOU SOAK A TOWEL AND TWIST IT UP INTO A WHIP. IT STINGS LIKE CRAZY AND IS MUCH WORSE THAN BEING COLD. GET MY DRIFT?

I ALWAYS THOUGHT LIFE-GUARDS WERE JUST TAUGHT HOW TO RESUSCITATE PEOPLE AND THINGS LIKE THAT.

THIS WATER IS FREEZING! I'M GOING TO GO INTO SHOCK AND DROWN, I JUST KNOW IT.

I BET THE LIFEGUARD IS INVOLVED IN SOME INSURANCE SCAM AND SHE'S GOING TO LET US ALL DROWN LIKE RATS! OH NO! OH NO!

OK, FIRST WE'RE GOING TO LEARN THE "DEADMAN'S FLOAT."

MOM!! HELPP! HELPP!

WHAT I PUT UP WITH TO PAY FOR COLLEGE..

I DON'T WANT TO LEARN HOW TO SWIM!

I DON'T NEED TO KNOW HOW. I'LL JUST STAY ON DRY LAND ALL MY LIFE.

WHAT IF YOU FALL OUT OF A BOAT?

NO BIG DEAL.

FORTY MINUTES OF TERROR! WHY DID YOU SIGN ME UP FOR THIS?

WHY NOT SOMETHING FUN, LIKE HANG GLIDING OR SHARPSHOOTING?

...OR *DRIVING* LESSONS! I COULD BE TAKING DRIVING LESSONS AND LEARNING SOMETHING USEFUL!

HOW ABOUT PIANO LESSONS? YOU START TUESDAY.

ACK! NO NO NO NO NO NO NO NO NO NO NO

CALVIN THE BUG BUZZES OFF!

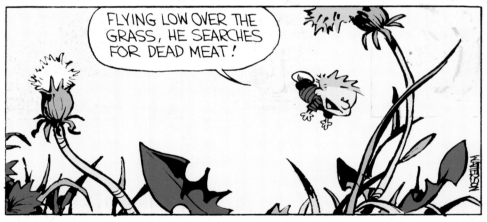

HI, CALVIN, WHAT ARE YOU DOING?

BIG IMPORTANT SECRET THINGS! GO AWAY! GET LOST!

ALL RIGHT, DANDELION HEAD! WHO CARES WHAT YOU DO ANYWAY!

WE'RE DOING GREAT THINGS. *WE'RE* HAVING *FUN!*

I THOUGHT WE WERE BORED OUT OF OUR SKULLS.

OH HUSH. YOU DON'T KNOW ANYTHING.

THAT STUPID CALVIN. HE'S SO MEAN.

ALL I TRY TO DO IS BE FRIENDS, AND HE TREATS ME LIKE I'M NOBODY.

WELL, WHO NEEDS JERKS LIKE HIM ANYWAY? I DON'T NEED HIM FOR A FRIEND. I CAN HAVE FUN BY MYSELF!

POOP.

SUSIE, HOBBES THOUGHT I WAS RUDE, SO I'M SORRY, AND YOU CAN COME PLAY WITH US IF YOU WANT.

THANKS, CALVIN. THAT'S REALLY NICE OF YOU.

OK, WE'LL PLAY HOUSE NOW. I'LL BE THE HIGH-POWERED EXECUTIVE WIFE, THE TIGER HERE CAN BE MY UNEMPLOYED, HOUSEKEEPING HUSBAND, AND YOU CAN BE OUR BRATTY AND BRAINLESS KID IN A DAY CARE CENTER.

THIS WAS *YOUR* IDEA, PEA BRAIN.

DON'T YOU TALK TO YOUR FATHER THAT WAY! I'M OFF TO WALL STREET. DON'T WAIT UP.

"ADD TWO EGGS AND STIR."

RIGHT.

THE RECIPE SAYS IT MAKES TWENTY PANCAKES, SO WE'LL EACH GET TEN.

NAH, THAT'S TOO MUCH TROUBLE.

WE'LL JUST MAKE ONE *BIG* PANCAKE AND CUT IT IN HALF.

DAD, I WANT A BEDTIME STORY!

I'M BUSY, CALVIN. I'LL READ YOU ONE TOMORROW.

IF YOU DON'T READ ME A STORY, I WON'T GO TO BED!

①Once upon a time there was a boy named Calvin, who always wanted things his way. One day his dad got sick of it and locked him in the basement for the rest of his life. Everyone else lived happily ever after.
The End.

I DON'T LIKE THESE STORIES WITH MORALS.

DINNER'S READY, CALVIN. COME TO THE TABLE.

I'M WATCHING TELEVISION.

NO, YOU'RE NOT!

YES, I AM. I'M RIGHT HERE IN FRONT OF IT!

NO YOU'RE *NOT!*

OH THAT'S RIGHT. I'M AT THE TABLE.

Calvin and Hobbes
by WATTERSON

WANNA TOSS THE OL' PIGSKIN AROUND?

HECK NO.

PHOOEY.

THE CENTER SNAPS THE BALL!

THE QUARTERBACK LOOKS FOR AN OPENING!

THE DEFENSE DISINTEGRATES BENEATH THE COMING ONSLAUGHT! THE QUARTERBACK JUMPS AND DODGES!

HOBBES BREAKS CLEAR!

CALVIN PASSES!

AN AMAZING CATCH! HOBBES IS AT THE 30... THE 20... THE 10...

...BUT HE'S TACKLED FROM BEHIND AND LATERALS TO CALVIN SO *HE* CAN MAKE THE TOUCHDOWN!

BUT CALVIN FUMBLES THE BALL AND HOBBES RECOVERS IT!

BUT A PENALTY IS CALLED ON THE PLAY AND HOBBES IS SENT TO THE BENCH!

HOBBES DEFECTS TO THE OTHER TEAM AND IS GREETED WITH ENTHUSIASTIC CHEERS! THE CROWD GOES WILD!

CALVIN PREPARES TO CRIPPLE THE TRAITOR WITH AN ILLEGAL FACE MASK PULL!

HOBBES DEFIES HIM BY POURING OUT HIS MOUTH GUARD ONTO CALVIN'S HELMET!

BOY, YOU CAN SEE WHY FOOTBALL IS SUCH A VIOLENT GAME!

HOBBES' TEAM GAINS A YARD! ALL THE CHEERLEADERS COME OUT FOR SMOOCHES!!

WATTERSON

Row 1

WITH A DRINK OF MAGIC ELIXIR, CALVIN TURNS HIMSELF INVISIBLE.

COMPLETELY TRANSPARENT, HE ROAMS UNDETECTED!

CALVIN?

BOY, AS SOON AS YOU WANT SOMETHING DONE AROUND HERE, THAT KID'S NOWHERE TO BE SEEN.

Row 2

HA HA! I HAVE TURNED MYSELF INVISIBLE!

BY REMOVING MY CLOTHING, I CAN PERPETRATE ANY CRIME UNDETECTED!

I HAVE COMPLETE FREEDOM! I CAN GET AWAY WITH ANYTHING!

CALVIN! WHAT ON EARTH ARE YOU DOING IN THE COOKIE JAR WITHOUT YOUR CLOTHES ON?!?

Row 3

YOUR POLLS ARE SLIPPING, DAD. BETTER GET WITH IT.

CALVIN, BEING YOUR DAD IS NOT AN ELECTED POSITION. I DON'T HAVE TO RESPOND TO POLLS.

NOT ELECTED? YOU MEAN YOU CAN GOVERN WITH DICTATORIAL IMPUNITY?

EXACTLY.

IN SHORT, OPEN REVOLT AND EXILE IS THE ONLY HOPE FOR CHANGE?

I DON'T LIKE THE DIRECTION THIS CONVERSATION IS TAKING..

Calvin and Hobbes

by WATTERSON

GRAVITY IS ARBITRARY!

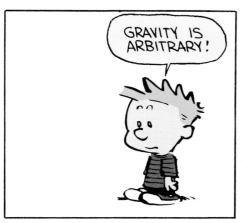

CALVIN WAKES UP ONE DAY TO FIND HE IS IMMUNE TO THE FORCE OF GRAVITY.

HE HANGS ON TO THE GROUND FOR DEAR LIFE, BUT HIS GRIP IS WEAKENING!

HE CAN'T HOLD ON! HE... HE **LETS GO!**

HIGHER AND HIGHER, AS UPWARD HE FALLS!

ONLY BY GRABBING THE TAIL FIN OF A PASSING JET DOES CALVIN SAVE HIMSELF FROM BEING HURLED OUT INTO SPACE!

WATTERSON

NO, NO, LET HIM FINISH. THIS IS VERY INTERESTING. SO AFTER YOU LANDED IN PHOENIX, WHAT HAPPENED?

WELL, I DON'T CARE. I'M NOT SEWING VELCRO ON THE OUTSIDE OF ALL HIS CLOTHES.

WELL, ABOUT THEN MY GRAVITY CAME BACK, SO I...

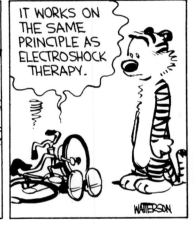

CRASH!

IT JUMPED ME!!

WATTERSON

LOOK, THERE'S A FROG!

C'MON, LET'S CATCH IT!

I'M NOT GETTING NEAR IT.

WHY NOT?

THEY DRINK WATER ALL DAY JUST IN CASE SOMEONE PICKS THEM UP.

I'M GOING TO HANG AROUND THE DRUGSTORE ALL AFTERNOON AND EAT CANDY AND READ COMIC BOOKS!

OH, NO, YOU'RE NOT!

WHY NOT?!

WATTERSON

BECAUSE I'M YOUR MOTHER AND I SAID SO. GET BACK IN HERE.

AND YOU CAN STOP GOOSE-STEPPING AROUND THE HOUSE!

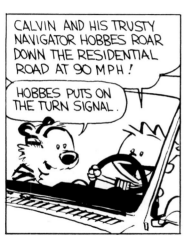

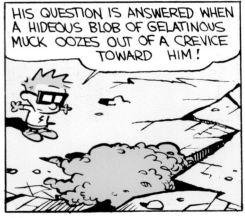

SUMMER VACATION'S OVER! NOTHING AHEAD BUT TOIL AND DRUDGERY FOR A WHOLE YEAR!

OH, COME ON, YOU SPENT HALF THE SUMMER COMPLAINING HOW BORED YOU WERE.

I DID?

YOU DID.

HOW STRANGE. I MUST HAVE BEEN DELIRIOUS FROM HAVING SO MUCH FUN.

I CAN'T BELIEVE IT! HOMEWORK ALREADY! I JUST GOT BACK TO SCHOOL!

I HAVE TO WRITE A PARAGRAPH ON WHAT I DID OVER THE SUMMER! *A WHOLE PARAGRAPH!!*

I'LL *NEVER* BE ABLE TO WRITE THAT MUCH! IT'S NOT *FAIR*!!

HOW'S IT COMING?

NOT SO GOOD. WHAT DID YOU DO BESIDES WATCH TV?

IN SOCCER, YOU CAN'T TOUCH THE BALL WITH YOUR HANDS OR ARMS.

SEE, YOU CAN USE ANY OTHER PART OF YOUR BODY...

...EVEN YOUR HEAD!

YEAH, BUT YOUR *FACE*?? DOESN'T THAT *HURT*?

RRRRGHH! THAT'S *NOT* WHAT I MEANT TO *DO*!

148

I HAVE A HYPOTHETICAL QUESTION. SUPPOSE A KID AT SCHOOL CALLED ME A NASTY NAME...

...SHOULD I KICK HIM REAL HARD IN THE SHINS?

NO, I DON'T THINK VIOLENCE WOULD BE JUSTIFIED.

HERE'S ANOTHER HYPOTHETICAL QUESTION. WHAT IF I ALREADY DID?

I'VE DECIDED TO GROW A BEARD, MOM.

A *LONG* BEARD. LIKE THE GUYS IN ZZ TOP.

THAT'S NICE, CALVIN. YOU GO AHEAD AND DO THAT.

I THOUGHT SHE'D PUT UP MORE OF A FUSS THAN THAT.

HOW ABOUT THESE PANTS, MOM? CAN I GET THESE?

GOOD HEAVENS, LOOK AT THE PRICE! *I* DON'T HAVE PANTS THAT COST THIS MUCH!

AND YOU'LL GROW RIGHT OUT OF THESE! HONESTLY, WHY WOULD ANY KID NEED DESIGNER CLOTHES??

"BABES."

BABES, MOM. I GOTTA LOOK COOL.

Calvin and Hobbes

by WATTERSON

QUIT SQUIRMING, CALVIN. YOU'VE GOT ICE CREAM ALL OVER YOUR SHIRT.

RATS, I WAS SAVING IT FOR LATER.

THANKS FOR THE ICE CREAM, DAD. IT WAS GREAT.

YOU'RE WELCOME.

I'M TIRED OF PULLING YOU. IT'S MY TURN TO RIDE.

YOUR DAD DIDN'T GET ME ANY ICE CREAM, SO I GET TO RIDE BOTH WAYS.

NO, YOU DON'T! DAD SAID TIGERS DON'T LIKE ICE CREAM! IT'S MY TURN TO RIDE!

TIGERS DON'T KNOW IF THEY LIKE ICE CREAM UNTIL THEY TRY EVERY KIND. I'M NOT PULLING.

I'VE GOT NEWS, FUZZ BRAIN. I'M NOT PULLING, EITHER!

WELL THEN, I GUESS WE'LL BOTH JUST SIT HERE UNTIL WE DIE.

WHY DO THESE "WALKS" ALWAYS END UP AS "RIDES"?

OH, YOU NEED THE EXERCISE MORE ANYWAY.

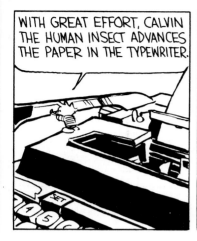

WITH GREAT EFFORT, CALVIN THE HUMAN INSECT ADVANCES THE PAPER IN THE TYPEWRITER.

HIS ONLY HOPE FOR PROPER MEDICAL TREATMENT LIES IN HIS ABILITY TO WRITE A LEGIBLE MESSAGE TO HIS FAMILY!

HE CRAWLS TO EACH KEY AND JUMPS!

WHO WROTE "HELP I'M A BUG" ON MY LETTER TO GRANDMA?

EVIDENTLY SOME BUG. HOW STRANGE.

BACK AND FORTH.

BACK AND FORTH.

TIDAL WAVE!

BEATS ME, MOM. MAYBE THE SEAL AROUND THE TUB LEAKS.

WHAT'S THIS MUSIC?

IT'S "THE 1812 OVERTURE."

I KINDA LIKE IT. INTERESTING PERCUSSION SECTION.

THOSE ARE CANNONS.

AND THEY PERFORM THIS IN CROWDED CONCERT HALLS?? GEE, I THOUGHT CLASSICAL MUSIC WAS BORING!

158

TOMORROW WE'RE GOING TO DISCUSS "CURRENT EVENTS" IN SCHOOL.

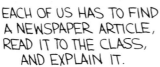

EACH OF US HAS TO FIND A NEWSPAPER ARTICLE, READ IT TO THE CLASS, AND EXPLAIN IT.

WHAT ARTICLE DID YOU CHOOSE?

THIS ONE.

"SPACE ALIEN WEDS TWO-HEADED ELVIS CLONE."

ACTUALLY, THERE'S NOT MUCH LEFT TO EXPLAIN.

LOOK WHAT YOU CAN DO WITH BIG SOCKS!

JUST PUT ONE OVER EACH EAR, AND ONE OVER YOUR NOSE...

AN ELEPHANT! HA HA! I WANT SOME SOCKS TOO!

IF I MISS THE BUS, IT'S GOING TO BE UNPLEASANT AROUND HERE!

CALVIN, HOW DID YOU BREAK THIS DISH?!

I WAS CARRYING TOO MUCH AND IT DROPPED.

YOUR PROBLEM IS YOU'VE GOT NO COMMON SENSE.

I'VE GOT **PLENTY** OF COMMON SENSE!

I JUST CHOOSE TO IGNORE IT.

LOOK, MOM, I PUT ALL MY CLOTHES FOR TOMORROW ON THE STAIRS.

THEN IN THE MORNING, I'LL RUN OUT IN MY UNDERWEAR AND SLIDE DOWN AT TOP SPEED!

IF I AIM GOOD, I GO RIGHT INTO MY PANTS WHILE I'M PUTTING ON MY SHIRT, AND BY THE BOTTOM, I'M ALL DRESSED FOR SCHOOL!

AND IF YOU PUT MY CEREAL ON THE STAIRS TOO, I WON'T HAVE TO GET UP UNTIL 30 SECONDS BEFORE THE BUS COMES.

FORGET IT, CALVIN.

WATTERSON

ACK   IGG

LOOK, MOM, I'VE GOT RABIES.

GO SPIT OUT YOUR TOOTHPASTE AND STOP BEING SILLY.

MAYBE DAD WILL FALL FOR IT IF I BITE HIM FIRST.

WATTERSON

WHAT ARE YOU GOING TO DRESS UP AS FOR HALLOWEEN?

I DON'T KNOW YET. I CAN'T DECIDE.

WATTERSON

WELL, THE IDEA IS TO BE THE SCARIEST THING YOU CAN THINK OF.

HMM...MAYBE I'LL JUST GO AS MYSELF!

I'M GOING AS A BARREL OF TOXIC WASTE!

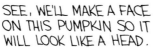
WE'RE GOING TO CARVE A JACK-O'-LANTERN NOW.

SEE, WE'LL MAKE A FACE ON THIS PUMPKIN SO IT WILL LOOK LIKE A HEAD.

BUT FIRST WE HAVE TO OPEN UP THE TOP AND SCOOP OUT THE GLOP INSIDE.

OK, JACK, TIME FOR YOUR LOBOTOMY!!

HAND ME A BIG SPOON, WILL YOU, HOBBES?

UGH! NO ANESTHETIC EVEN.

WATTERSON

I THINK DAD LIKES HALLOWEEN AS MUCH AS WE DO.

IS HE TAKING US TRICK OR TREATING TONIGHT?

NO, MOM IS.

IS HE GOING TO STAY HOME AND GIVE OUT CANDY?

NO, HE'S GOING TO SIT IN THE BUSHES WITH THE GARDEN HOSE AND DRENCH POTENTIAL T.P.'ERS.

OOG, I FEEL AWFUL.

IF SOMEONE EVEN MENTIONS "MILK DUDS," I'M GONNA BARF.

WATTERSON

ANOTHER HALLOWEEN COME AND GONE.

IT'S ALWAYS SUCH A LETDOWN AFTER A HOLIDAY.

WE MIGHT AS WELL GO INTO TOWN AND LOOK AT THE CHRISTMAS DECORATIONS.

MOM'S NOT FEELING WELL, SO I'M MAKING HER A "GET WELL" CARD.

THAT'S THOUGHTFUL OF YOU.

SEE, ON THE FRONT IT SAYS, "GET WELL SOON."

AND ON THE INSIDE IT SAYS, "BECAUSE MY BED ISN'T MADE, MY CLOTHES NEED TO BE PUT AWAY, AND I'M HUNGRY."

"LOVE, CALVIN." WANT TO SIGN IT?

SURE. I'M HUNGRY TOO.

HI, MOM! SINCE YOU'RE SICK, I'M BRINGING YOU BREAKFAST IN BED!

I PREPARED EGGS, TOAST AND ORANGE JUICE FOR YOU ALL BY MYSELF!

HOW NICE!

THE EGGS KIND OF BURNED AND STUCK TO THE PAN, BUT YOU CAN PROBABLY CHIP THEM OUT WITH THIS CHISEL.

UM... WHERE IS THE TOAST AND ORANGE JUICE?

DAD SAID NOT TO TELL YOU ABOUT THAT TILL YOU'RE BETTER.

SINCE YOUR MOM'S SICK, I'LL BE MAKING DINNER TONIGHT.

YOU CAN COOK?

OF COURSE I CAN COOK.

AS YOU CAN SEE, I SURVIVED TWO YEARS OF MY OWN COOKING WHEN I HAD AN APARTMENT AFTER COLLEGE.

MOM SAYS YOU ATE FROZEN WAFFLES AND CANNED SOUP THREE MEALS A DAY.

YOUR MOM WASN'T THERE, SO SHE WOULDN'T KNOW. GET THE SYRUP OUT, WILL YOU?

SOMETIMES WHEN *I'M* SICK, YOU READ ME A STORY. WANT ME TO READ *YOU* ONE?

NO, THANKS, CALVIN. I JUST WANT TO REST.

IT'S HARD TO BE A MOM FOR A MOM.

YOU DO FINE, SWEETIE.

WHOA! HEY! ARE YOU CONTAGIOUS?

WHAT'S WRONG WITH YOUR MOM, DO YOU KNOW?

NO. SHE WENT TO THE DOCTOR TODAY, THOUGH.

I WONDER IF... NAH.

WHAT?

YOU DON'T SUPPOSE SHE'S GOING TO HAVE A BABY, DO YOU?

A BABY?!?

WHY WOULD SHE WANT ANOTHER KID?? SHE'S ALREADY GOT *ME!*

YES, YOU'D THINK SHE'D HAVE LEARNED HER LESSON...

I ASKED DAD IF MOM WAS GOING TO HAVE A BABY, AND HE SAID NOT THAT *HE* KNEW OF.

DAD SAID WE'D KNOW IF MOM WAS HAVING A KID BECAUSE SHE'D LOOK LIKE A HIPPOPOTAMUS WITH A GLAND PROBLEM.

...THAT'S WHEN MOM CREAMED HIM WITH HER PILLOW.

DAD SAYS SHE MUST BE FEELING BETTER.

YOU HAVE WEIRD PARENTS.

HEY, MOM, I GOT A PART IN THE CLASS PLAY!

I GET TO SAY A LINE, AND EVERYTHING!

THAT'S WONDERFUL, CALVIN.

IT'S A GREAT DRAMATIC ROLE! MY CHARACTER WILL HAVE EVERYONE IN TEARS AT THE END OF THE SECOND ACT!

WHAT'S THE PLAY?

"NUTRITION AND THE FOUR FOOD GROUPS." I'M AN ONION.

OK, HOBBES, I NEED YOU TO HELP ME MEMORIZE MY LINE FOR THE PLAY.

SURE.

I'M THE ONION, AND I SAY, "IN ADDITION TO SUPPLYING VITAL NUTRIENTS, MANY VEGETABLES ARE A SOURCE OF DIETARY FIBER."

OK, READY?

READY. GO AHEAD. "IN ADDITION..."

WAIT. HOLD IT. I'M NOT IN CHARACTER YET. WHAT MOTIVATES AN ONION?

FAME, I SUPPOSE. THIS COULD BE A BIG BREAK.

OK, YOU BE "BREAD." PROMPT ME.

"GLUCOSE IS THE BODY'S MAIN ENERGY SOURCE!"

"IN ADDITION..." UH... UM... "IN ADDITION.." UM... WAIT..

GRRRGHH! I HATE THIS PLAY! I'LL NEVER BE ABLE TO LEARN THIS STUPID PART!

WELL, YOUR EMOTING IS DOWN PAT.

Panel 1:
I'VE GOT IT ALL FIGURED OUT, HOBBES. THIS PLAY WILL BE NO SWEAT.

Panel 2:
YOU HAVE YOUR LINE ALL MEMORIZED?

Panel 3:
NO, I THOUGHT I'D COME OUT, DO A LITTLE SOFT-SHOE, AND AD-LIB SOMETHING!

Panel 4:
AD-LIB SOMETHING ABOUT DIETARY FIBER?

EITHER THAT, OR I'LL DO MY ONION IN MIME!

Panel 5:
HOW'S MY ONION COSTUME COMING, MOM?

Panel 6:
I'M STILL WORKING ON IT. I WISH YOUR CLASS WOULD DO SOMETHING A LITTLE LESS ELABORATE. I'M NOT MUCH OF A SEAMSTRESS.

Panel 7:
JUST BE GLAD I'M NOT RUSSY WHITE. *HE* HAS TO BE AN AMINO ACID.

Panel 8:
MM... WHAT DO YOU THINK?

JABBA THE HUTT MEETS RUDOLF THE REINDEER. I DUNNO, MOM.

Panel 9:
ARE YOU GOING TO COME TO MY PLAY, DAD? IT'S CALLED "NUTRITION AND THE FOUR FOOD GROUPS."

Panel 10:
I'LL PROBABLY HAVE TO BE AT WORK, CALVIN.

BUT DAD, IT'LL BE GREAT DRAMA! I'M AN ONION!

Panel 11:
WELL, WHY DON'T YOU SAY YOUR LINE FOR ME NOW?

OK! UM... ..LET'S SEE.. "IN ADDITION TO..." ..UH... HOLD IT... UM..

Panel 12:
25 KIDS IN FOOD SUITS, FORGETTING THEIR LINES. I'LL *DEFINITELY* BE AT WORK.

DEAR! CALVIN'S WORKED HARD.

OK, UH... "IN ADDITION.."..UH NO, WAIT.. UM...

I CAN'T BELIEVE IT! I'M STUCK IN MY ONION SUIT!

I CAN'T GO ONSTAGE WITH MY SHIRT CAUGHT IN MY COSTUME! HELP! HELP!

I'M SUPPOSED TO BE ON NOW! I'M SUPPOSED TO BE SAYING MY LINE! WHAT SHOULD I DO?? WHAT SHOULD I DO??

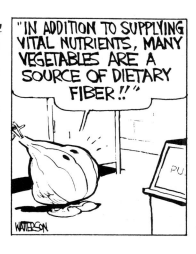

"IN ADDITION TO SUPPLYING VITAL NUTRIENTS, MANY VEGETABLES ARE A SOURCE OF DIETARY FIBER!!"

I'M HOME!

HI, HONEY. HOW DID YOUR PLAY GO?

TERRIBLE. I GOT STUCK IN MY ZIPPER IN THE BATHROOM, AND THEY HAD TO STOP THE PLAY AND GET A JANITOR TO FIND ME AND GET ME OUT.

OH NO. THAT'S AWFUL!

I'LL SAY... THE PLAY WAS RUINED.

...BUT I REMEMBERED MY LINE!

UP, UP AND AWAY!

WOOMPH!

ACKK! KRYPTONITE! KRYPTONITE!

175

Calvin and Hobbes by Watterson

OP ZIP ZOP ZIP ZOP ZIP ZOP ZIP ZOP ZIP ZOP ZIP ZOP ZIP ZOP

SNOW PANTS.

WELL? LET'S HAVE SOME SNOW!!

IT'S SNOWING! I CAN MAKE IT SNOW! I'M PSYCHOKINETIC! HEY! HEY!

OOH, HE'S GOING TO HATE ME FOR THIS.

IT'S HARD TO BELIEVE PEOPLE STILL STARVE IN THIS WORLD.

THERE'S EVEN HUNGER IN AMERICA.

SOME PEOPLE NEVER GET ENOUGH TO EAT.

BOY, I KNOW WHAT *THAT'S* LIKE!

NO YOU DON'T.

THE SOLDIERS ADVANCE UP THE HILL!

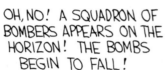

OH, NO! A SQUADRON OF BOMBERS APPEARS ON THE HORIZON! THE BOMBS BEGIN TO FALL!

BONK BONK

TWO DIRECT HITS!

I SEE YOU UP THERE!

LOOK, HOBBES, YOU GET A PLASTIC TRINKET IN BOXES OF "CHOCOLATE-FROSTED SUGAR BOMBS"!

IT SAYS, "BE THE FIRST IN YOUR NEIGHBORHOOD TO COLLECT ALL TEN COLORS."

YEAH, BUT MOM SAYS SHE WON'T BUY ANY MORE CEREAL UNTIL THIS BOX IS GONE.

THAT SHOULDN'T TAKE MORE THAN A COUPLE HOURS, RIGHT?

I DUNNO. AFTER FIVE BOWLS, I GET PRETTY WIRED.

Calvin and Hobbes
by WATTERSON

A BRILLIANT BOLT OF DEADLY FRAP RAY BLAZES BY THE INTREPID SPACEMAN SPIFF!

OUR HERO HAS VERY HIGH INSURANCE PREMIUMS.

THE COURAGEOUS SPACEMAN SPIFF IS HIT! HE PLUMMETS TOWARD PLANET ZOG!

BREAKING THROUGH THE CLOUD LAYER, HE CAREENS OVER AN ALIEN CITY! THERE'S NO PLACE TO LAND!

SPIFF WRESTLES THE UNCOOPERATIVE CONTROLS! MORE FREEM DRIVE TO THE THRUSTER BLASTERS!

TOO MUCH STRESS! THE FUEL EXPLODES IN FLAME!

THE SITUATION IS GRIM! TEN SECONDS TO IMPACT! NINE.... EIGHT...

WELL, CALVIN??

SEVEN!

VERY GOOD, CALVIN. TEN MINUS THREE EQUALS SEVEN. I DIDN'T THINK YOU WERE PAYING ATTENTION. THAT QUESTION WAS WORTH THREE POINTS.

OUR HERO MIRACULOUSLY MAKES A THREE-POINT LANDING. SPIFF SAVES THE DAY AGAIN!

WATTERSON

I'VE GOT A GREAT IDEA FOR SCHOOL TOMORROW.

I CUT A PING-PONG BALL IN HALF, AND NOW I'M DRAWING DOTS ON EACH END.

I'LL JUST PUT ONE OVER EACH EYE, AND IT WILL LOOK LIKE I'M REALLY PAYING ATTENTION.

...OR WILL I LOOK *TOO* INTERESTED?

I DOUBT IT. I'M OVER HERE.

BAD NEWS ON YOUR POLLS, DAD.

YOU SLIPPED ANOTHER TWO NOTCHES. THINGS ARE LOOKING GRIM FOR FUTURE OFFICE.

IS THAT SO?

ANY IDEAS ON WHAT WOULD IMPROVE MY STANDINGS?

I NEED A VCR.

RIGHT. I'LL KEEP THAT IN MIND.

I HOPE YOU'RE READING THE "HELP WANTED" SECTION.

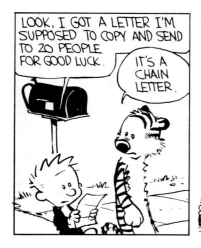
LOOK, I GOT A LETTER I'M SUPPOSED TO COPY AND SEND TO 20 PEOPLE FOR GOOD LUCK.

IT'S A CHAIN LETTER.

IT SAYS, "A MAN IN DENVER MADE 20 COPIES AND THE NEXT DAY HE GOT A RAISE. A MAN IN SEATTLE BROKE THE CHAIN AND HE WENT BALD."

HA! YOU BELIEVE THAT? THESE LETTERS ARE FOR SUPERSTITIOUS NINCOMPOOPS. THROW IT AWAY.

"...AND A DUMB KID LIKE YOU LISTENED TO A FRIEND AND GOT RUN OVER BY A CEMENT MIXER."

Calvin and Hobbes
by WATTERSON

Calvin: I'M READY FOR BED, DAD. WHAT'S TONIGHT'S STORY GOING TO BE?

Dad: HERE'S ONE. "READINGS ON DIALECTICAL METAPHYSICS." YOU'LL LOVE IT.

Calvin: FORGET IT, DAD. YOU CAN'T GET ME TO DROP OFF *THAT* EASY.

Calvin: WILL YOU READ US *THIS* STORY? HOBBES WROTE IT HIMSELF.

Dad: HOBBES WROTE IT, HUH?

Dad: "GOLDILOCKS AND THE THREE TIGERS."

Calvin: OH BOY, THIS IS GONNA BE GREAT!

Dad: "ONCE UPON A TIME THERE LIVED A YOUNG GIRL NAMED GOLDILOCKS. SHE WENT INTO THE FOREST AND SAW A COTTAGE. NO ONE WAS HOME SO SHE WENT IN."

Dad: "INSIDE SHE SAW THREE BOWLS OF PORRIDGE. A BIG BOWL, A MEDIUM BOWL, AND A SMALL BOWL. SHE WAS JUST ABOUT TO TASTE THE PORRIDGE WHEN THE THREE TIGERS CAME HOME."

Dad: "THEY QUICKLY DIVIDED GOLDILOCKS INTO BIG, MEDIUM, AND SMALL PIECES AND DUNKED THEM IN THE PORRIDGE THAT..."

Dad: CALVIN, I'M NOT GOING TO FINISH THIS! THIS IS DISGUSTING!!

Dad: I DON'T KNOW WHY I LET YOU TALK ME INTO THIS. *GOOD NIGHT!*

CLICK

Calvin: HE DIDN'T EVEN LOOK AT OUR ILLUSTRATIONS.

Hobbes: NOW I'M ALL HUNGRY.

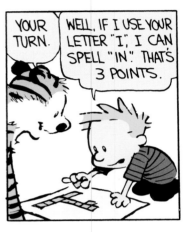

CALVIN HAS MYSTERIOUSLY SHRUNK TO THE SIZE OF AN INSECT!

HIS ONLY HOPE IS TO CALL FOR HELP! PUSHING WITH ALL HIS MIGHT, CALVIN DIALS THE GIGANTIC TELEPHONE!

DEF 3 ABC 2

IT'S RINGING! HE RUNS TO THE MOUTHPIECE! WILL ANYONE BE ABLE TO HEAR HIM??

BZZ BZ! BZZZZ! BZZ BZZ! BZZZ BZ!

CALVIN, THIS HAD BETTER NOT BE YOU.

WATTERSON

FWOOSHHH

GREETINGS, EARTH FEMALE. DO NOT BE ALARMED.

OUR PLANET IS DYING. WE NEED COOKIES TO SURVIVE. DO NOT TRY TO RESIST OR YOU WILL BE DESTROYED.

WE'LL SEE ABOUT THAT. GET BACK HERE.

WHY DO I HAVE TO GO TO BED NOW? I NEVER GET TO DO WHAT I WANT!

IF I GROW UP TO BE SOME SORT OF PSYCHOPATH BECAUSE OF THIS, YOU'LL ALL BE SORRY!!

WATTERSON

NOBODY EVER BECAME A PSYCHOPATH BECAUSE HE HAD TO GO TO BED AT A REASONABLE HOUR.

YEAH, BUT YOU WON'T LET ME CHEW TOBACCO EITHER! YOU NEVER KNOW WHAT MIGHT PUSH ME OVER THE BRINK!

GO TO BED, CALVIN.

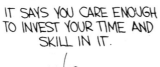

BEHOLD THE DREADED TOBOGGAN: SUICIDE SLED.

ITS UNIQUE DESIGN SENDS A BLINDING SPRAY OF SNOW ON ITS PASSENGERS AT THE SLIGHTEST BUMP. NOTE, TOO, THE LACK OF ANY STEERING MECHANISM.

YES, THIS SLED IS TRULY A HAZARD TO LIFE AND LIMB.

WHEEE OOMPH! EEEEE

WATTERSON

BOY, IS IT COLD! CAN'T WE TURN THE HEAT UP?

HEAT IS EXPENSIVE, CALVIN. JUST PUT ON A SWEATER.

LOOK, THE THERMOSTAT GOES ALL THE WAY UP TO 90 DEGREES! WE COULD BE SITTING AROUND IN OUR SHORTS!

LEAVE THE THERMOSTAT ALONE, CALVIN.

I CAN ALMOST SEE MY BREATH. I'LL JUST CRANK IT UP TO 75, OK?

I SAID DON'T TOUCH IT!

GEE, MY HANDS ARE SO NUMB, I CAN'T MOVE THE SWITCH. GUESS I'LL PUT ON A SWEATER.

WATTERSON

OOH, YOU LOOK COLD, CALVIN! THERE'S A FIRE MADE. WHY DON'T YOU GO WARM UP?

OH BOY!

NOTHING BEATS SITTING BY A ROARING FIRE AFTER YOU'VE BEEN OUT IN THE COLD.

WATTERSON

OF COURSE, SOME PEOPLE SAY WHY BOTHER GOING OUTSIDE FIRST?

Z

CALVIN, I HOPE YOU TOOK YOUR BOOTS OFF BEFORE YOU WALKED ACROSS THE FLOOR.

OF COURSE I DID! YOU DON'T NEED TO TELL ME ALL THE TIME!

GIVEN ANY MORE THOUGHT TO THAT BACKYARD SKI LIFT PROPOSAL OF MINE?

OH, YES. LOTS.

HOBBES IS ALWAYS A LITTLE LOOPY WHEN HE COMES OUT OF THE DRYER.

WHIFFFFF...○

WHIFF
WHIFF
WHIFF
WHIFF
WHIFF

FOR ALL THAT PREPARATION, YOU SURE ARE A LOUSY SHOT!

GO AHEAD DOWN. YOU'LL MISS ALL THOSE TREES.

YOU CAN DO IT. YOU'LL STOP BEFORE YOU GO OVER THAT LEDGE AT THE BOTTOM.

YOU WON'T GO INTO THAT POND. BESIDES, THE ICE IS PROBABLY REAL THICK ANYWAY. GO AHEAD DOWN.

MY BRAIN IS TRYING TO KILL ME.

GALOSH
GALOSH
GALOSH

I CALLED SUSIE A BOOGER-BRAIN AFTER SCHOOL, AND SHE WENT HOME CRYING.

GOODNESS, WHY'D YOU DO *THAT*?

I DUNNO. I WAS JUST TEASING.

IT SOUNDS LIKE YOU HURT HER FEELINGS.

I DIDN'T MEAN FOR HER TO TAKE THE INSULT *PERSONALLY!*

SNIFF THAT STUPID CALVIN. WHY DOES HE CALL ME NAMES FOR NO REASON? IT'S JUST MEAN.

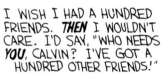

I WISH I HAD A HUNDRED FRIENDS. *THEN* I WOULDN'T CARE. I'D SAY, "WHO NEEDS *YOU*, CALVIN? I'VE GOT A HUNDRED OTHER FRIENDS!"

THEN MY HUNDRED FRIENDS AND I WOULD GO DO SOMETHING FUN, AND LEAVE CALVIN ALL ALONE! HA!

...AND AS LONG AS I'M DREAMING, I'D LIKE A PONY.

I FEEL BAD THAT I CALLED SUSIE NAMES AND HURT HER FEELINGS.

I'M SORRY I DID IT.

MAYBE YOU SHOULD APOLOGIZE TO HER.

I KEEP HOPING THERE'S A LESS OBVIOUS SOLUTION.

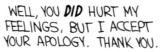

201

WELL, WELL! IT'S AN INVITATION TO SUSIE DERKINS' BIRTHDAY PARTY. HOW NICE.

SUSIE INVITED *YOU*? WHAT ABOUT ME? DOES IT SAY ME TOO?

NO, IT DOESN'T SAY ANYTHING ABOUT YOU.

SHE MUST HAVE MAILED MY INVITATION SEPARATELY. SHE PROBABLY WANTED TO INSURE IT SO SHE'LL KNOW IT DIDN'T GET LOST. SOMETIMES THOSE TAKE LONGER.

I'LL HAVE TO SIGN FOR IT AND ALL. I'M SURE SHE'S TAKING NO CHANCES WITH MINE.

OH WAIT. ON THE BACK IT SAYS, "YOU CAN BRING THAT STUPID KID YOU HANG AROUND WITH, IF YOU MUST."

WE GET TO GO TO A BIRTHDAY PARTY!

THAT STUPID SUSIE.

BALLOONS, CAKE, PRESENTS... OH BOY!

SHE WON'T BE GETTING A VERY BIG PRESENT FROM *ME*, THAT'S FOR SURE.

I BET WE'LL PLAY GAMES, TOO! IT WILL BE FUN!

HMPH.

MAYBE WE'LL PLAY "SPIN THE BOTTLE"!

OH GET REAL!

I'LL MAKE A LIST OF POSSIBLE GIFTS FOR SUSIE'S BIRTHDAY. WHAT SHOULD WE GIVE HER?

HOW ABOUT A MOUTH FULL OF BROKEN TEETH? THAT'S WHAT *I'D* LIKE TO GIVE HER.

OH, DON'T BE SO CRANKY.

I THINK WE SHOULD GET HER A CAN OF TUNA FISH.

TUNA FISH? WHY WOULD SHE WANT *THAT*?

WELL, MAYBE SHE WOULDN'T, AND WE COULD OFFER TO TAKE IT BACK..... AND BORROW SOME BREAD, A LITTLE MAYO ...

RIGHT, HOBBES.

SUSIE'S HOUSE IS THE NEXT ONE UP.

THIS IS OUR LAST CHANCE TO NOT SHOW UP AND HAVE A NEW BIKE HORN.

HI, SUSIE. HAPPY BIRTHDAY!

HELLO, CALVIN. THANKS FOR COMING.

OH, LOOK AT YOUR STUFFED TIGER! HE'S WEARING A TIE!

HE'S JUST *ADORABLE!*

OK, YOU WERE RIGHT. GIRLS FLIP FOR TIES. YOU CAN STOP WINKING AT ME.

C'MON IN.

OK, EVERYONE, THE IDEA OF A SCAVENGER HUNT IS TO BRING BACK AS MANY OF THESE ITEMS AS YOU CAN IN HALF AN HOUR. LET'S GO!

QUICK, HOBBES, WHAT'S THE FIRST ITEM?

AN OLD LICENSE PLATE.

GREAT! I SAW ONE ON THE WAY OVER! C'MON!

GOOD THING I ALWAYS CARRY A SWISS ARMY KNIFE. NOBODY'S COMING, RIGHT?

IS THIS GAME LEGAL?

HERE'S A PAPER PLATE FOR THE BIRTHDAY CAKE, CALVIN.

THANK YOU.

I HOPE IT'S GOOD. I HATE IT WHEN THE BIRTHDAY KID CHOOSES SOMETHING GROSS LIKE COCONUT.

YOU DON'T HAVE TO WORRY. IT'S CHOCOLATE.

OH, GOOD. DID YOU SEE IT?

HEY! WHO CUT A PIECE OF MY CAKE ALREADY?! I DIDN'T EVEN GET TO BLOW OUT THE CANDLES!!

IT'S NICE AND MOIST, TOO.

GLAD YOU BOTH COULD COME. THANK YOU FOR THE NICE PRESENT. GOOD-BYE.

MOM MAY NOT WANT THIS PIECE OF CAKE AND ICE CREAM WE'RE BRINGING HER.

HEY! IT SNOWED LAST NIGHT!

OH, BOY! LOOK AT IT ALL! THEY'LL HAVE TO CLOSE THE SCHOOLS!

SNOW EVERYWHERE! IT MUST BE WAIST DEEP!

UNFORTUNATELY, THAT'S A RELATIVE MEASURE.

CALVIN AND HOBBES

by WATTERSON

WHY CAN'T I EVER FIND MY STUPID SCARF?

HOBBES AND I ARE GOING OUTSIDE, MOM.

THIS IS GOING TO BE THE BIGGEST SNOWMAN EVER BUILT!

PEOPLE WILL COME FROM MILES TO SEE OUR GIGANTIC SNOWMAN!

THIS WON'T GO ANY MORE. IT'S TOO BIG TO PUSH.

OK, LEAVE IT HERE.

I'M EXHAUSTED!

WELL WE CAN'T STOP NOW! WE NEED NINE MORE OF THESE!

NINE MORE?!

SURE! THIS IS JUST ONE OF HIS TOES!

WHERE DO WE KEEP ALL OUR CHAINSAWS, MOM?

WE DON'T HAVE ANY CHAINSAWS, CALVIN.

WE DON'T? NOT ANY?

NOPE.

HOW AM I EVER GOING TO LEARN HOW TO JUGGLE?

THE GIANT AMOEBA SLIDES ALONG THE KITCHEN FLOOR.

EXTENDING A CYTOPLASMIC PSEUDOPOD, THE PROTOZOAN ENGULFS A PACKAGE OF OATMEAL COOKIES.

CRUNCH CRUNCH

NICE TRY. PUT THEM BACK.

THE MAJESTIC EAGLE CIRCLES SLOWLY IN THE CLOUDS.

WITH EYES SO SHARP HE CAN SPOT MOVEMENT A MILE BELOW, HE SIGHTS HIS PREY AND DIVES!

REACHING SPEEDS OF MORE THAN 100 MPH, HIS UNWARY PRIZE WILL NEVER KNOW WHAT HIT IT!

WAKE UP, DAD! IT'S SATURDAY!

ZZ... WHA?

Calvin and Hobbes

by WATTERSON

HERE IS SUCCESSFUL MR. JONES. HE LIVES IN A 5-ACRE HOME IN A WEALTHY SUBURB. HERE IS HIS NEW MERCEDES IN THE DRIVEWAY.

IT'S ANYONE'S GUESS AS TO HOW MUCH LONGER MR. JONES CAN MEET HIS MONTHLY FINANCE CHARGES.

HERE COMES MR. JONES OUT OF HIS ATTRACTIVE SUBURBAN HOME. HE HOPS IN HIS RED SPORTS CAR.

OFF HE GOES TO WORK. 80...90... 100 MILES AN HOUR!

...ALONG THE EDGE OF THE GRAND CANYON!!

SUDDENLY, HIS STEERING LOCKS AND HIS BRAKES FAIL! HE CAREENS OVER THE EDGE! OH NO! DOWN HE GOES!

HIS ONLY HOPE IS TO CLIMB OUT THE SUN ROOF AND JUMP! MAYBE, JUST MAYBE, HE CAN GRAB A BRANCH AND SAVE HIMSELF! HE UNWINDS THE SUN ROOF! CAN HE MAKE IT??

NO! THE CAR EXPLODES IN MID-AIR, PROPELLING MILLIONS OF TINY SHARDS INTO THE STRATOSPHERE! KABLOOIE!

THE NEIGHBORS HEAR THE BOOM ECHOING ACROSS THE CANYON. THEY PILE INTO A MINI-VAN TO INVESTIGATE! WHAT WILL HAPPEN TO THEM?

OH, MOM, I NEED SOME CRISCO FOR SCHOOL TODAY!

SHORTENING? HONESTLY, CALVIN, I WISH YOU'D REMEMBER THESE THINGS THE NIGHT BEFORE. NOW HURRY UP AND GET READY.

RIGHT.

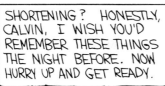

HERE'S THE CRISCO BACK. THANKS.

YOU PUT IT IN YOUR HAIR??

GET BACK HERE! YOU'RE NOT GOING TO SCHOOL LIKE THAT!

AW C'MON, MOM! IT'S CLASS PICTURE DAY!

WHAT'S WITH YOUR HAIR?

I TOLD MOM I'M GETTING MY SCHOOL PICTURE TAKEN TODAY, AND SHE MADE ME COMB OUT THE CRISCO I PUT IN MY HAIR. NOW I LOOK LIKE A MORON.

THAT'S TRUE. YOU DO.

WELL DON'T JUST STAND THERE! THINK OF SOMETHING! WHAT CAN I DO?

THERE. MUCH BETTER!

WHAT'D YOU DO? IS IT COOL? IS IT NEW WAVE? GEE, I WISH I HAD A MIRROR...

THE BUS IS GOING TO BE HERE ANY MINUTE. YOU'RE SURE YOU FIXED MY HAIR SO IT LOOKS OK?

IT LOOKS GREAT. TRY NOT TO MUSS IT UP.

YOU'RE NOT KIDDING ME, ARE YOU? THIS REALLY LOOKS GOOD?

TRUST ME. YOU LOOK LIKE ... LIKE...

..."ASTRO BOY."

ALL RIGHT! I CAN'T WAIT TO GET MY PICTURE TAKEN NOW!

CALVIN! WHAT DID YOU DO TO YOUR HAIR?? DON'T YOU KNOW WE HAVE OUR PICTURES TAKEN TODAY?

OF COURSE, SILLY. THAT'S WHY I DID IT. IT'S CRISCO.

DOES YOUR MOM KNOW YOU LOOK LIKE THAT?

SORT OF. HOBBES FIXED ME UP A LITTLE AT THE BUS STOP.

WOW. I WISH *I* HAD SOME CRISCO.

WAIT TILL MOM SENDS MY PICTURE TO GRANDMA!

OK, KID, SIT UP STRAIGHT ON THE STOOL AND LOOK RIGHT AT ME. THAT'S IT.

ARE YOU READY TO TAKE MY PICTURE? SHOULD I TAKE OFF MY SHIRT NOW?

KID, WHAT ARE...? DON'T TAKE OFF YOUR SHIRT!!

SEE? I PAINTED A FACE ON MY STOMACH.

KID, PUT YOUR SHIRT BACK ON.

BUT LOOK! WHEN I BREATHE OUT, THE FACE CHANGES! SEE? OK, TAKE ONE QUICK!

LOOK, HOBBES, I GOT MY SCHOOL PICTURES BACK.

LOOK AT YOU! HA HA HA! LOOK AT YOUR HAIR! HEE HEE! THESE ARE GREAT!

AREN'T THEY, THOUGH?

HEE HEE HEE! LOOK AT THIS ONE! WHAT AN EXPRESSION! HOO HOO HOO! HA HA!

YEAH, SEE HOW I GOT MY ONE EYE TO ROLL BACK?

HA HA HA! YOUR MOTHER'S GOING TO GO INTO CONNIPTIONS, OF COURSE..

OH, C'MON. YEARS FROM NOW, THINK OF THE MEMORIES THESE WILL BRING.

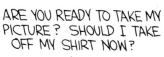

Calvin and Hobbes

by WATTERSON

GLIK
GLIK
GLIK

OH NO! WHAT HAVE I DONE?!?

THE HUMAN BODY IS 80% WATER. LITTLE DID CALVIN REALIZE HOW CRITICAL IT IS TO MAINTAIN THAT!

NOW IT'S TOO LATE! BY DRINKING THAT EXTRA GLASS OF WATER, CALVIN HAS UPSET THAT PRECIOUS BALANCE! HE IS NOW **90%** WATER!

EVERYTHING SOLID IN CALVIN'S BODY BEGINS TO DISSOLVE!

HE IS BECOMING A LIQUID!!

HIS ONLY HOPE IS SOMEHOW TO GET TO AN ICEBOX AND FREEZE HIMSELF SOLID UNTIL HE CAN GET PROPER MEDICAL ATTENTION!

UNFORTUNATELY, AS A LIQUID, CALVIN CAN ONLY RUN DOWNHILL! CAN HE MAKE IT? CAN HE MAKE IT??

I DON'T THINK I'M GONNA MAKE IT.

THERE'S A GAS STATION UP AHEAD. JUST HOLD ON.

DIDN'T I TELL YOU NOT TO DRINK SO MUCH BEFORE WE LEFT?!

I'M HOME!

I THOUGHT THAT AFTER SEVEN BORING HOURS AT SCHOOL, YOU MIGHT APPRECIATE ONE MOMENT OF PURE, ABJECT TERROR.

LET ME UP TO GET MY BAT AND I'LL THANK YOU.

HOBBES, LOOK! THERE'S A LITTLE RACCOON ON THE GROUND.

IS IT ALIVE?

I THINK SO, BUT HE'S HURT. SEE, HE'S HARDLY BREATHING.

BETTER NOT TOUCH HIM IF HE'S HURT.

YEAH. YOU WAIT HERE AND GUARD HIM. I'LL RUN AND GET MOM.

I SURE HOPE SHE CAN HELP.

OF COURSE SHE CAN! YOU DON'T GET TO BE MOM IF YOU CAN'T FIX EVERYTHING JUST RIGHT.

THERE'S HOBBES GUARDING HIM, MOM. THE LITTLE RACCOON'S RIGHT OVER THERE!

OOH, CALVIN, I DON'T KNOW IF WE CAN SAVE HIM. HE LOOKS PRETTY BAD. GO GET A SHOE BOX AND A CLEAN DISH TOWEL.

RIGHT!

I DON'T THINK THIS POOR LITTLE GUY IS GOING TO MAKE IT, HOBBES. (SIGH) I HATE IT WHEN THESE THINGS HAPPEN.

...YOU CAN TELL I'M UPSET WHEN I START TALKING TO YOU...

WELL, I GOT HIM IN THE SHOE BOX. I GUESS ALL WE CAN DO IS KEEP HIM WARM AND SAFE.

WE'LL KEEP HIM IN THE GARAGE, AND PUT OUT SOME WATER AND FOOD.

I READ IN A BOOK THAT RACCOONS WILL EAT JUST ABOUT ANYTHING.

CHANCES ARE, I'LL BE HAPPY TO DONATE MOST OF MY DINNER.

CALVIN, YOU DON'T EVEN KNOW WHAT WE'RE HAVING.

THIS IS WHERE DAD BURIED THE LITTLE RACCOON.

I DIDN'T EVEN KNOW HE EXISTED A FEW DAYS AGO AND NOW HE'S GONE FOREVER. IT'S LIKE I FOUND HIM FOR NO REASON. I HAD TO SAY GOOD-BYE AS SOON AS I SAID HELLO.

STILL... IN A SAD, AWFUL, TERRIBLE WAY, I'M HAPPY I MET HIM.

SNIFF

WHAT A STUPID WORLD.

YOU KNOW, HOBBES, I CAN'T FIGURE OUT THIS DEATH STUFF.

WHY DID THAT LITTLE RACCOON HAVE TO DIE? HE DIDN'T DO ANYTHING WRONG.

HE WAS JUST LITTLE! WHAT'S THE POINT OF PUTTING HIM HERE AND TAKING HIM BACK SO SOON ?!?

IT'S EITHER MEAN OR IT'S ARBITRARY, AND EITHER WAY I'VE GOT THE HEEBIE-JEEBIES.

WHY IS IT ALWAYS NIGHT WHEN WE TALK ABOUT THESE THINGS?

MOM SAYS DEATH IS AS NATURAL AS BIRTH, AND IT'S ALL PART OF THE LIFE CYCLE.

SHE SAYS WE DON'T REALLY UNDERSTAND IT, BUT THERE ARE MANY THINGS WE DON'T UNDERSTAND, AND WE JUST HAVE TO DO THE BEST WE CAN WITH THE KNOWLEDGE WE HAVE.

I GUESS THAT MAKES SENSE.

...BUT DON'T YOU GO ANYWHERE.

DON'T WORRY.

HEY! WHAT HAPPENED TO THE TREES HERE? WHO CLEARED OUT THE WOODS?

THERE USED TO BE LOTS OF ANIMALS IN THESE WOODS! NOW IT'S A MUD PIT!

THIS SIGN SAYS, "FUTURE SITE OF SHADY ACRES CONDOMINIUMS."

ANIMALS CAN'T AFFORD CONDOS!

"SHADY ACRES"? THE ONLY SHADE *I* SEE IS FROM THAT BULLDOZER.

WATTERSON

WHERE ARE ALL THE ANIMALS SUPPOSED TO LIVE NOW THAT THEY CUT DOWN THESE WOODS TO PUT IN HOUSES ??

BY GOLLY, HOW WOULD *PEOPLE* LIKE IT IF ANIMALS BULLDOZED A SUBURB AND PUT IN NEW *TREES* ?!?

WATTERSON

NO GOOD. THEY DIDN'T LEAVE THE KEYS.

IT TOOK HUNDREDS OF YEARS FOR THESE WOODS TO GROW, AND THEY LEVELED IT IN A WEEK. IT'S GONE.

AFTER THEY BUILD NEW HOUSES HERE, THEY'LL HAVE TO WIDEN THE ROADS AND PUT UP GAS STATIONS, AND PRETTY SOON THIS WHOLE AREA WILL JUST BE A BIG STRIP.

EVENTUALLY THERE WON'T BE A NICE SPOT LEFT ANYWHERE.

I WONDER IF YOU CAN REFUSE TO INHERIT THE WORLD.

I THINK IF YOU'RE BORN, IT'S TOO LATE.

WATTERSON

Calvin and HObbes

by WATTERSON

KABLOOIE!

OOOOH, YOU'VE TWICKED ME FOR THE WAST TIME, WABBIT!

HA HA HA! BOY, I WISH *I* HAD SOME DYNAMITE!

BOY, I LOVE WEEKENDS! WHAT BETTER WAY TO SPEND ONE'S FREEDOM THAN EATING CHOCOLATE CEREAL AND WATCHING CARTOONS!

MM... I BEG TO DIFFER ON THE CEREAL PART.

CALVIN, YOU'VE BEEN SITTING IN FRONT OF THAT STUPID TV ALL MORNING! IT'S A BEAUTIFUL DAY! YOU SHOULD BE OUTSIDE!

IT'S GOING TO BE A GRIM DAY WHEN THE WORLD IS RUN BY A GENERATION THAT DOESN'T KNOW ANYTHING BUT WHAT IT'S SEEN ON TV!

click

HEY!

HOW CAN YOU SIT INSIDE ALL DAY? GO ON! OUT! OUT!

KIDS ARE SUPPOSED TO RUN AROUND IN THE FRESH AIR! HAVE SOME FUN! GET SOME EXERCISE!

WATTERSON

SLAM!

WELL, I GUESS THAT'S THAT. COME ON.

HI, SUSIE, ARE YOU WATCHING TV? CAN WE COME IN?

SURE, HURRY UP! IT'S A COMMERCIAL.

Calvin and Hobbes

by WATTERSON

Look, Jane. See Spot.
See Spot run.
Run, Spot, run.
Jane sees Spot run.

WAY TO GO, JANE!

BOY, I HATE HOMEWORK.

YAHH!

WHOOP!

HEY!

YOW! WHOA! STOP!

GALOOP GALOOP

AAAUGHH!!

GAACKK! HELP! HELP!

WHAP!!

BONK!

BONK!

WHAT ON EARTH ARE YOU *DOING?* WHERE'S YOUR HOMEWORK?

I COULDN'T CONCENTRATE.

RRINNGGG!

RECESS IS OVER!

R-R-RIPP!

SNAG

OH NO!

WHY IS IT YOU ALWAYS RIP YOUR PANTS ON THE DAY EVERYONE HAS TO DEMONSTRATE A MATH PROBLEM AT THE CHALKBOARD?

WATTERSON

I CAN'T BELIEVE I RIPPED MY PANTS! RECESS IS OVER. I'M SUPPOSED TO BE BACK IN CLASS!

I CAN'T GO IN LIKE THIS! WHAT AM I GOING TO DO??

...OF ALL THE DAYS TO WEAR THE UNDERPANTS WITH THE LITTLE ROCKET SHIPS...

WATTERSON

LOOK AT THE SIZE OF THIS RIP! MAYBE I CAN PULL MY SHIRT DOWN OVER IT.

NO, THAT DOESN'T WORK. MAYBE I CAN TUCK MY SHIRT INTO THE HOLE. ..NOPE..

MAYBE I CAN STICK THE RIPPED PART UNDER MY BELT. NO, THAT DOESN'T WORK EITHER.

WATTERSON

MAYBE I CAN SCOOT AROUND ON MY REAR THE REST OF THE DAY.

CALVIN and HOBBES
by WATTERSON

"DURING EMERGENCY LANDING, REPLACE DINNER TRAY AND BRING SEAT TO UPRIGHT POSITION. EXTINGUISH ALL SMOKING MATERIALS."

"...INCLUDING SPACECRAFT, IF POSSIBLE."

OUT OF FUEL, THE COURAGEOUS SPACEMAN SPIFF IS FORCED TO LAND ON THE DISTANT PLANET ZOK!

THE VALIANT EXPLORER SURVEYS THE ZOKKIAN LANDSCAPE. WHO KNOWS WHAT DANGERS LIE HIDDEN IN THE CRATERED TERRAIN?

UNDAUNTED, SPIFF SETS OUT TO FIND HELP!

MILES LATER, IT IS EVIDENT THE PLANET IS COMPLETELY UNINHABITED!

OUR HERO IS MAROONED ON A LIFELESS PLANET! ALONE ON AN ALIEN WORLD!

ALONE... ALL ALONE...

DARN IT, WHY DOESN'T ANYONE EVER **TELL** ME WHEN THE LUNCH BELL RINGS?

SUSIE, WHERE'S MISS WORMWOOD? WHO'S THAT LADY AT HER DESK?

MISS WORMWOOD'S SICK. THAT'S OUR SUBSTITUTE TEACHER.

A SUBSTITUTE?

LET'S SEE YOUR TEACHING CERTIFICATE, LADY!

GOOD MORNING, CLASS. I'LL BE YOUR SUBSTITUTE TEACHER TODAY.

MISS WORMWOOD LEFT ME INSTRUCTIONS AS TO WHAT WE NEED TO GO OVER, SO WE SHOULDN'T HAVE ANY PROBLEMS.

OH WAIT, HERE'S A NOTE SHE ADDED. JUST A SECOND...

OK, WHICH ONE OF YOU IS CALVIN?

NOT ME!

WE HAD A SUBSTITUTE TEACHER IN SCHOOL TODAY.

DID YOU LIKE HER?

SHE WAS OK, I GUESS.

YOU "GUESS"?

IT'S HARD TO SAY.

SHE WENT HOME AT NOON.

Mr. Jones lives 50 miles away from you. You both leave home at 5:00 and drive toward each other.

Mr. Jones travels at 35 mph., and you drive at 40 mph. At what time will you pass Mr. Jones on the road?

GIVEN tHe TRaffic around HeRe at 5:00, WHo KNowS?

I ALWAYS CATCH THESE TRICK QUESTIONS.

I'VE GOT A SCHEME TO GET US SOME MONEY.

OH BOY.

SEE? I SNEAKED ALL THESE KERNELS OF CORN OFF MY DINNER PLATE TONIGHT.

HOW IS THAT GOING TO GET US MONEY?

EASY. I JUST STICK THEM UNDER MY PILLOW.

WITH ANY LUCK, THE TOOTH FAIRY WON'T KNOW THEY'RE FAKES UNTIL IT'S TOO LATE!

DAD, HOW DO PEOPLE MAKE BABIES?

MOST PEOPLE JUST GO TO SEARS, BUY THE KIT, AND FOLLOW THE ASSEMBLY INSTRUCTIONS.

I CAME FROM SEARS??

NO, YOU WERE A BLUE LIGHT SPECIAL AT K MART. ALMOST AS GOOD, AND A LOT CHEAPER.

AAUUGHHH!

DEAR, WHAT ARE YOU TELLING CALVIN NOW?!

I'VE GOT TO GIVE A 5-MINUTE ORAL REPORT IN SCHOOL ON THURSDAY.

WE'RE SUPPOSED TO RESEARCH OUR SUBJECT, WRITE IT UP, AND PRESENT IT TO THE CLASS WITH A VISUAL AID.

THAT'S A BIG ASSIGNMENT.

I'LL SAY. I HATE MY TEACHER.

SHE KNOWS WE'LL ALL DO IT ON THE LAST EVENING, BUT SHE GAVE US THREE DAYS TO WORRY ABOUT IT.

WHAT'S THE SUBJECT OF YOUR REPORT?

THE BRAIN.

WHAT DO YOU KNOW ABOUT BRAINS?

WELL, I SAW THIS MOVIE WHERE THEY KEPT THIS GUY'S BRAIN ALIVE IN A TANK OF WATER.

THEN A POWER SURGE MUTATED THE BRAIN, AND IT CRAWLED OUT AND TERRORIZED THE POPULACE.

THAT'S INFORMATIVE.

UNFORTUNATELY FOR MY REPORT, MOM CAUGHT ME, AND I DIDN'T GET TO SEE HOW IT ENDED.

I'VE GOT TO GIVE MY REPORT ON "THE BRAIN" AT SCHOOL TODAY.

SEE MY VISUAL AID? I COOKED SOME NOODLES AND PUT THEM IN A PAPER BAG. DOESN'T THAT LOOK LIKE BRAINS?

UGH.

WELL, I GUESS I'M ALL SET.

DID YOU WRITE YOUR REPORT YET?

NAH. I BORROWED MOM'S POCKET DICTIONARY. I'LL DO IT ON THE BUS.

 MY FIVE-MINUTE REPORT IS ON "THE BRAIN."

 OF COURSE, IT'S DIFFICULT TO EXPLAIN THE COMPLEXITIES OF THE BRAIN IN JUST FIVE MINUTES, BUT TO BEGIN, THE BRAIN IS PART OF THE CENTRAL NERVOUS SYSTEM.

 I'LL PAUSE FOR A FEW MOMENTS, SO YOU ALL CAN FINISH WRITING THAT DOWN. CALVIN!

 POW! JAB! KICK! POW! POW!

 RATTATATTATATTA RATTATATTATTA

 EEEEEEEEEEE BOOM!

 PLEASE, PLEASE, PRETTY PLEASE? NO. YOU SHOULD'VE SAVED SOME OF YOUR OWN HALLOWEEN CANDY.

 HEY, CAN WE CHANGE THE CHANNEL NOW? I WANT TO WATCH SOMETHING ELSE.

 MY SHOW'S NOT OVER YET. AW C'MON! YOU SEE THIS PROGRAM ALL THE TIME! CAN'T WE WATCH MY SHOW FOR ONCE?

 NO, I WAS HERE FIRST. PIPE DOWN. THIS IS A GOOD PART. AARRGHH

 I HATE NATIONAL GEOGRAPHIC ANIMAL SPECIALS.

Calvin and Hobbes

by WATTERSON

Point A is twice as far from point C as point B is from A. If the distance from point B to point C is 5 inches, how far is point A from point C?

THE LIVING DEAD DON'T **NEED** TO SOLVE WORD PROBLEMS.

CALVIN THE ZOMBIE SEARCHES FOR FOOD.

HORRIBLY, THE UNDEAD FEED UPON THE LIVING!

...ALTHOUGH, IN A PINCH, A PBJ WILL DO, IF YOU EAT IT MESSILY ENOUGH.

"WHEN IN ROME..."

WELL, YOUR HAIR DOESN'T STICK UP THE WAY IT USED TO, BUT AT LEAST YOUR HEAD'S YELLOW AGAIN.

THANKS, HOBBES. YOU'RE A REAL LIFE SAVER. I'M SORRY I GOT SO MAD AT YOU.

NONSENSE. NO HARM DONE.

BOY, WAIT TILL I SHOW MOM!

UH OH. DOES IT COME OFF?

FROM NOW ON, JUST KEEP YOUR BRAINY IDEAS TO YOURSELF, OK?

WATTERSON

calvin

calvin the GENIUS

calvin the SUPER GENIUS

THIS IS HOW YOU SIGN YOUR REPORTS?

IT KIND OF INCLINES YOU TO READ IT MORE CHARITABLY, DON'T YOU THINK?

WATTERSON

CLINK CLINK

MY ICED TEA IS A FAILURE.

WATTERSON

Calvin and Hobbes

by WATTERSON

THIS IS SUPPOSED TO BE GREAT ART.

...SO WHY DOES IT LOOK LIKE A BUNCH OF DECAPITATED NAKED PEOPLE?

A STRANGE FEELING COMES OVER CALVIN IN THE ART MUSEUM.

HIS PARENTS, ENGROSSED IN CULTURE, REMAIN BLISSFULLY UNAWARE OF CALVIN'S TERRIBLE TRANSFORMATION!

YES, A TYRANNOSAURUS IS LOOSE IN THE ART MUSEUM! THE CURATOR SHRIEKS, AND PANDEMONIUM ENSUES!

A GUARD REACHES FOR HIS PISTOL, BUT THE DINOSAUR IS UPON HIM AND HE IS MESSILY DEVOURED!

THE GIANT LIZARD'S GLORY IS CAPTURED FOREVER ON FILM BY THE ANTI-THEFT CAMERAS! PATRONS OF THE ARTS FLEE FOR THEIR LIVES!

HUNDREDS OF PRICELESS PAINTINGS ARE RIPPED TO SHREDS IN THE AWFUL RAMPAGE! WEALTHY BENEFACTORS ARE TRAMPLED! THE MUSEUM IS IN RUINS! ON TO SYMPHONY HALL!!

CALVIN? ... CALVIN? WE'RE IN THE NEXT ROOM NOW. C'MON.

I THINK WE'D BETTER GET HIM OUT OF HERE. HE HAD THAT GRIN AGAIN.

I WANNA SEE THE DINOSAURS AT THE NATURAL HISTORY MUSEUM AGAIN.

WE SPENT ALL AFTERNOON THERE, CALVIN.

The End